D1283806

Teaching General Mathematics

TEACHERS' MATHEMATICS REFERENCE SERIES

Bruce E. Meserve, Series Editor

Hight	A CONCEPT OF LIMITS
Parker	THE STRUCTURE OF NUMBER SYSTEMS
Pettofrezzo	MATRICES AND TRANSFORMATIONS
Pettofrezzo	VECTORS AND THEIR APPLICATIONS
Smith	EXPLORATIONS IN ELEMENTARY MATHEMATICS
Sobel	TEACHING GENERAL MATHEMATICS

PRENTICE-HALL INTERNATIONAL, INC., London
PRENTICE-HALL OF AUSTRALIA, PTY. LTD., Sydney
PRENTICE-HALL OF CANADA, LTD., Toronto
PRENTICE-HALL OF INDIA PRIVATE LTD., New Delhi
PRENTICE-HALL OF JAPAN, LTD., Tokyo

Max A. Sobel

Professor of Mathematics
Montclair State College, New Jersey

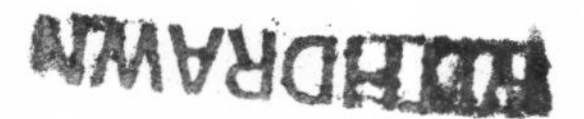

TEACHING GENERAL MATHEMATICS

A SOURCE BOOK OF IDEAS
FOR
TEACHING THE SLOW LEARNER

PRENTICE-HALL, INC., ENGLEWOOD CLIFFS, NEW JERSEY

Library of Congress Catalog Card Number
67-22740

Current printing (last digit):
10 9 8 7 6 5 4 3 2

Printed in the United States of America

To Manya–
for learning to live
with a very slow learner

Series Foreword

EACH BOOK of this series is concerned with an important topic or area of the mathematical training of teachers. The exposition follows the highly successful pattern of the Meserve-Sobel books. There are many illustrative examples to facilitate the use of the books for individual study and in-service programs. There are numerous exercises to provide an opportunity for readers to develop their understanding. The answers to the odd-numbered exercises are in the back of each book; the answers to the even-numbered exercises are available in a separate booklet. Thus each book is designed to serve as a text either in an in-service program or in a college course for prospective teachers or others interested in extending their knowledge of these mathematical concepts. Some of the books are particularly useful as supplementary texts in college and advanced high-school courses.

The topics for these books have been selected because of their significance in the rapid evolution of our contemporary mathematics curricula. Each author has tested his materials in preliminary form with hundreds and (in at least one case) thousands of college students and/or school teachers. Briefly, this series consists of books on significant topics presenting tested materials in a manner that has been proved to be highly effective.

The brevity of the books is purposeful. Each book may be used as a supplementary reference text in a more extensive or advanced course. Each book provides the basis for an extensive unit of work in an in-service, college, or school course. Considerable flexibility in meeting the needs of the students is available by using two or more of these books in an extensive course or series of courses.

Frequent additions of books to this series are contemplated.

Bruce E. Meserve, Series Editor

Preface

THE UNITED STATES has been involved, since the advent of Sputnik, in what has commonly been called a "revolution" in school mathematics. Development of scientifically trained manpower has been the major objective of various foundations as they have poured money into curriculum groups working on programs for the college capable student. Almost totaly neglected in the first decade of this furor have been students of average and below average ability, including low achievers as well as slow learners. In this text, we shall refer to all of them as slow learners even though low achievers are not necessarily slow learners.

Through the years there have been sporadic attempts to cope with the problems of the slow learner in mathematics. Frequently, lack of funds has been the cause of abortive attempts to develop programs for these groups of youngsters. As a result, the task of providing an adequate program of mathematics for the slow learner remains as one of the most serious and persistent problems for teachers of mathematics in our junior and senior high schools. Many teachers in junior colleges, community colleges, and small colleges have a similar problem. In fact, in most colleges, teachers of mathematics face this problem since many people with considerable talents in other fields appear to be slow learners in mathematics. This makes the teaching of mathematics for general education a problem of increasing social and cultural significance in our scientific age.

In this source book we shall explore three phases of the problem of the slow learner in mathematics:

(1) Who is the slow learner? What are his basic characteristics and needs? How can he best be motivated? What procedures should be followed to guide the learning activities of the slow learner?

(2) What experiments have been conducted, and what programs are available for the slow learner? What attention has been given to the problems of the slow learner by professional organizations and by national curriculum study groups?
(3) What specific units of study can a teacher develop that are educationally and mathematically worthwhile and that can be used to meet the needs of the slow learner?

I have long been interested in the problem of the slow learner. As a junior and senior high school teacher I came to appreciate the slow learner's problems and frustrations, as well as the teachers' dilemma in trying to meet their students' needs. The materials in this text are the result of my experience with these students, with teachers who have been in my college graduate courses, and with special workshops designed to explore the problem of providing a program of mathematics for the slow learner.

To Bruce E. Meserve, my consulting editor, and very good friend, I owe my deep gratitude and appreciation for inspiring me to undertake this task, for providing so many helpful and constructive suggestions, and for stimulating me to complete the manuscript. To my wife, Manya, I owe another vote of thanks for her patient understanding during many long hours of neglect. Finally, I wish to thank the editors of Prentice-Hall for their undying confidence in the Meserve-Sobel combination!

Max A. Sobel

Contents

chapter 1

The Slow Learner

The term "slow learner" has been and is being used in a variety of different ways by different people. General education courses in mathematics at all levels are designed for students who have not felt the need of or have not prepared themselves for formal courses in mathematics. We shall find it convenient to refer to these students as slow learners even though their low achievement may have been for a variety of reasons. Since we are using the term "slow learner" to include a wide variety of students, we first consider the group under discussion and examine their basic characteristics and needs. Later we shall consider mathematics curricula for these students.

1-1 Identifying the Slow Learner

Many terms have been used in educational circles to describe the youngsters in our classes who are below average in their ability to learn mathematics. We speak of the "low achiever," the "slow learner," the "nonacademic student," as well as use other less flattering terms. At a 1964 conference sponsored by the U.S. Office of Education in cooperation with the National Council of Teachers of Mathematics [26]†, the following definition was cited:

> The low achiever in mathematics is that student who, by teacher estimates, achievement tests, or by whatever means the school uses for marking, grouping, or promotion, *ranks below the 30th percentile of the student population in achievement in mathematics.*

---

†Numbers in brackets refer to references at the end of the book.

In terms of IQ there is no fixed magic score to identify the slow learner. Almost every teacher has had the experience of failing a student with an IQ of 125 and working exceptionally well with one who had an IQ of 90! However, in general, the term slow learner is applied to the group with IQ's in the range of 75 to 90. A mean IQ of 85 is yet another way to describe the intellectual level of this group.

In his text *Education for the Slow Learners* [19], Johnson asserts that 15% to 18% of the school population can be considered to be slow learners. He points out that these students are not able to learn academic skills at the same chronological age at which they are taught to others; but they may be able to learn such skills at a later date after having achieved additional mental maturity. On the other hand, being slow, they will never be capable of complete learning and thus should not be thought of as "late bloomers" who will eventually catch up to others in their mental development. These students are an important part of the student body in our general education courses in junior and senior high schools.

There are numerous references in the literature, such as [6], to the problem of identifying the slow learner. It is suggested that one pay attention to such items as IQ, past performance in arithmetic, teacher recommendations, reading ability, and results on standardized tests. The classroom teacher, however, need not be overly concerned with this problem of identification. Regardless of whether a student is a slow learner, a low achiever, or both, the major concern of the classroom teacher is to understand the student and to make provisions for him in the classroom.

Our need to provide a meaningful curriculum for all low achievers is no longer debatable. Indeed the conference previously cited operated under the following assumptions:

(1) Our nation needs the potential manpower of the low achiever in mathematics.
(2) Low achievers will not be qualified for future employment unless they learn more mathematics than is the case now.
(3) The mathematics ability of the low achiever can be developed to the extent necessary for a saleable skill.
(4) The low achiever should have the mathematics instruction necessary for (a) a saleable skill and (b) a rich cultural citizenship.

Our society has a need for productive citizens and is also committed to a democratic concern for all individuals. The teacher of mathematics has a role to play in this process, as well as a selfish interest in providing for the slow learner in terms of self-preservation. We need to provide an adequate program for this group of students or else possibly jeopardize our chances for survival in the classroom!

1-2 Characteristics and Needs of the Slow Learner

Let us now turn our attention to some of the basic characteristics and needs of the slow learner. The emphasis on the teaching of mathematics has always been on the logical systematic development of subject matter. All too often the psychological basis for learning has been neglected. For the slow learner, and especially in the junior high school, the psychological emphasis is perhaps more important than the selection of specific mathematical topics. What are some of these psychological considerations? As a start, consider the following list of characteristics and needs of all adolescents:

(1) In the first place, these are the years of rapid, uneven growth and there is a need for both teachers and students alike to understand this growth and to realize that it is both variable and individual in nature.
(2) Youngsters of this age, continuing a drive which begins at birth, seek personal independence from both parents and teachers.
(3) They seek peer acceptance and have a need to belong to some social group.
(4) They are insecure, primarily due to the tremendous physical changes taking place at this age, and crave security and success.
(5) They want recognition, approval, status.
(6) Their interests change rapidly; they crave new experiences while at the same time longing for the security of the old.

These basic characteristics and needs are common to all adolescents and should be kept in mind by all teachers. However, it is absolutely essential that attention be given to these needs by teachers of slow learners inasmuch as these students have difficulty in making adjustments because of their limited mental abilities. Abraham [2] summarizes these needs quite dramatically when he writes of the three A's: *Acceptance*, *Affection*, *Achievement*. We will have gone a long way in providing for the slow learners once we have learned to meet these three of their basic needs.

Developing a mathematics curriculum based on the psychological needs of the slow learner leads directly to several basic observations. First of all, it is important to build on prior mathematical experiences so as to lead to a sense of security. *A careful and slow graduation of the mathematical difficulty of the material studied is essential.* Too radical an increase leads to trial-and-error behavior in order to find some scheme to succeed and thus gain security.

Whereas all students crave security and have a need to succeed, the slow learner is especially vulnerable in this respect. Years of consistent failure in the early grades make him vulnerable to all sorts of *meaningless trial-and-error* schemes just to get an answer and satisfy the demands of the teacher.

It is important that we make an effort to *motivate the student.* During adolescence there is resistance to learning unless the subject matter is of interest to the student and meaningful to him; again, the slow learner can become especially resistant unless his interest, dulled by years of failure, is aroused. Specific ways of arousing this interest will be considered later. It can be said, however, that we cannot interest these youth by deluging them with huge quantities of social applications, using the excuse that these are of practical value. Some may be; most are not. We need to present honest-to-goodness mathematics to them in an organized and systematic structure, but in a manner that will evoke their interest and natural curiosity.

Adolescents in general, and slow learners in particular, are eager to grasp and adopt patterns of work providing them with security and independence. *Thus they are prone to learn tricks and meaningless manipulations in order to achieve success.* Students given numerous problems to solve by rote tend to repeat these methods in tasks that can be solved by more direct means. This rigidity of thinking, following of patterns, does not place a stress on thinking or on basic concepts; rather, it places a premium on obtaining answers.

To summarize briefly; the slow learner, especially in the junior high school, has the same characteristics as other students of the same age; he has the same basic needs and interests. However, more than the average person, he needs to be given the chance to experience success and approval; more than the others, he needs to feel that he is a member of the group with a contribution to make; he needs status; his confidence must be reestablished, his interest stimulated, his attitude toward mathematics made favorable, his ego flattered.

1-3 Guiding the Learning Activities of the Slow Learner

It is appropriate now to set forth a number of specific suggestions that are important in guiding the learning activities of the slow learner. Whereas many of the items to be listed apply to all youth, they are of special importance with respect to the slow learner in mathematics.

Psychological Considerations

Achievement of slow learners should be measured in terms of individual growth. It makes no sense, and it frustrates both teacher and child alike, to try and evaluate students with many years of deficiencies in terms of a preconceived standard of what should be accomplished in a particular grade. It is obvious, for example, that most slow ninth graders are not able to do the equivalent of what we consider to be ninth grade work. Marks on the basis of the expected attainments of average ninth grade students are usually futile, frustrating, and fruitless.

Successful student materials should be exhibited to provide a feeling of accomplishment. The slow learner seldom has an opportunity to experience success. Therefore, when he hands in a good homework paper or obtains a good grade on a test, the teacher should boost his morale by displaying these materials on a bulletin board. Another good way to boost morale is to give an occasional test or quiz on which almost every youngster will be able to score 100%; slow learners do not have this delightful experience very often.

Never embarrass a student in front of his classmates. No adolescent, especially one who is a slow learner, can afford to lose face with his peers. Specific suggestions, criticism, or advice should be offered privately. Many of the discipline problems that arise with groups of slow learners are brought on by the teacher who chastises a youngster in front of his fellow students.

Expect homework; otherwise the slow learner loses respect for the course and begins to feel like a second-class citizen. Of course such assignments will almost invariably have to be started in class and possibly finished there. Assignments need to be short, concrete, and based upon previously learned materials. In short, the teacher must make sure that the student can indeed do the assigned work.

Develop course prestige. We need to develop and build the self-respect of the student. He knows that he is a slow learner; he has often experienced years of frustration and failure. The only way to rebuild his self-esteem is to provide a curriculum that is not an obvious rehash of elementary mathematics and that excites his imagination. Specific recommendations along this line will be made later.

Methods of Presentation

The activities of the slow learner must be varied because of his short attention span. Too often the new, inexperienced teacher neglects this item and frequently meets with disastrous results. Projects, laboratory work, board work, supervised study, and recitation must be mixed in liberal dosages. Of course teachers will have to be discreet in their use of such activities if class control is a problem. In such cases, it is well to keep the students suitably occupied throughout the period and provide very little opportunity for movement around the classroom.

Concrete presentations must be emphasized. Laboratory techniques and manipulative materials are essential. The use of visual aids, models, films, and filmstrips can play an important part in the education of these students.

A spiral development of topics is essential. It is not sufficient to teach a topic just once. Frequent reviews are necessary. Do not expect the slow learner to retain what he has learned for any great length of time, with the possible exception of certain of the basic arithmetic skills.

Subject matter should be correlated with work in other classes whenever possible. This helps develop a feeling of security on the part of the student. For example, when the science teacher is studying the solar system, we in the mathematics classroom can make scale drawings of the planets, represent the distances to the planets on graphs, and solve problems using data discussed in the science classroom.

Practical applications should be included. Although there are also other procedures for gaining the interest of, or for motivating, this group, this approach should not be neglected.

Drill is essential, but it must not be based solely on rote memorization. Drill must be varied so that improper mental sets are not established. The slow learner, more so than others, must understand what he is doing.

Verbal materials in the text must be developed orally. We cannot assume comprehension of reading; the slow learner is, more often than not, retarded in this area as well.

Projects and activities must be short, with the goal in sight. The student should see the purpose of an activity.

Instructions must be very specific and clear. General assignments to "study" or "review" are meaningless and confusing to the slow learner.

Frequent short tests (quizzes) are highly recommended. Such tests of material recently covered are preferred over large unit evaluations. The span of retention for the slow learner is short, and tests that cover too much material can only lead to frustration.

Verbalization may not be necessary. Slow learners have difficulty verbalizing their thoughts. If you are able to lead them to a discovery, be content if they are able to display an unverbalized awareness of a concept.

The slow learner does best in a laboratory type setting, where he can be led to make simple discoveries on his own. As indicated earlier, discipline problems may arise more readily in such situations, so classroom control must be assured before this setting is used. A laboratory type setting should noticeably facilitate the use of a discovery approach in teaching slow learners and thus provide one of the most rewarding aspects of their education.

Start the course with new and significant subject matter. At each grade level, the procedure used to start the course is of crucial importance. Most slow learners in the junior high school are in dire need of a meaningful reteaching of arithmetic. As a matter of fact, this should be the fundamental work of these grades. On the other hand, experience indicates that beginning the work of a year with this much-needed review of arithmetic tends to destroy any interest that might otherwise be aroused. Similar problems arise at other grade levels. Much of this text is devoted to the exposition of specific suggestions concerning this item.

Classroom Management

Routines need to be established for classroom management. In his need for security, the slow learner appreciates and does best in a situation where routines have been established for such items as homework, tests, distribution and collection of materials, and use of texts and supplies. That is, the slow learner needs to know exactly what is to be expected of him. But there still should be room in such a program for occasional deviations and surprises in order to avoid boredom.

It is important to get a class started on time. New teachers find this one of their most serious problems. Here too, routines will help. One proven technique is to have a predetermined spot on the blackboard where the teacher has written instructions for the first five minutes of work of each period. This may tell the student to do a problem in his notebook, to take a quiz, etc. At any rate, this procedure may be used to settle the class quickly at the start of a period, and it gives the teacher time to get organized for the day's lesson.

New teachers are especially concerned over problems of discipline that seem to arise quite readily and often in classes of slow learners. There are many sources which offer suggestions on maintaining good discipline [13], [30]. However, the best way to prevent discipline problems from arising is to keep the student suitably occupied throughout each period with a meaningful, interesting, and challenging curriculum. This point of view will be explored further in the next chapter where we shall review briefly the attempts made to date to provide materials for the slow learner.

1-4 Summary

A major problem that still remains is that of providing a meaningful curriculum for the slow learner. Despite the student's failure to learn the fundamentals of arithmetic in the elementary grades, we frequently organize a curriculum for him that repeats the same materials in the same way in the junior high school, in the senior high school, and in many of our colleges. It is almost as though we felt that constant exposure to the same routine, dull, and unimaginative content would eventually produce skill in these fundamentals. Not only does this routine drill fail to produce skill, it also succeeds in killing any interest these youngsters may have had for mathematics. For the low achiever, such a program proves to be dull, deadly, and destructive of all interest—with ensuing discipline problems. Alternatives to such routine procedures will be explored in the chapters to follow.

Overlooked in almost all of the literature dealing with slow learners are their personal opinions of themselves. In a very interesting study by the New Jersey Secondary School Teachers Association [28], a survey was conducted of both slow learners and teachers of such groups. As may be expected, the teachers believe that slow learners have more serious social problems and have more of a failure orientation than other students. On the other hand, the slow learners themselves claim otherwise! The gloomy point of view of the teachers was in sharp contrast to the optimistic views of the slow learners.

This study points up the need for teachers who understand the slow learner and his problems. Of all the personal qualities needed by teachers of slow learners, patience is by far the one most frequently cited. Many other traits can also be listed, such as sympathy, friendliness, sense of humor, imagination, fairness, firmness, tolerance, and respect for others.

Questions for Discussion

1. What are the minimum mathematical competencies that should be expected of all high school graduates?
2. Make a list of as many traits as you can that should be possessed by teachers of slow learners.
3. Explore and compare the general mathematics curriculum in at least two junior high schools, at least two senior high schools, and at least two colleges.
4. Add as many items as you can to the list of guiding principles presented in §1-3 under psychological considerations, under methods of presentation, and under classroom management.
5. List five topics which you believe to be suitable for use at the start of the year with a group of slow learners to develop course prestige at the seventh grade level, at the ninth grade level, at the twelfth grade level, and in college.
6. Examine and discuss the marking procedures used in general mathematics classes in your school. Compare this with practices of other schools.
7. Read and comment upon the check list of functional competence in mathematics as prepared by the Commission on Post-War Plans [4].

chapter 2

Survey of Related Curriculum Developments

Through the years a number of groups have made determined efforts to explore the problem of the slow learner and to establish programs of mathematics suitable for such students. We shall examine the results of several of the more recent of these efforts.

2-1 NCTM Secondary-School Curriculum Committee

The National Council of Teachers of Mathematics (NCTM) established a Secondary-School Curriculum Committee to explore and report upon various aspects of the mathematics curriculum [27]. A subcommittee was formed in 1958 to study the adjustment of the mathematics program to pupils of average and below-average ability. The report of this group was incorporated into the overall report of the committee, and it presented a number of teaching suggestions such as the following:

(1) Generalizations, in order to be understood by the class, must be preceded by many and varied concrete illustrations.
(2) Frequent reviews in meaningful situations are necessary in order to maintain a reasonable level of skill and understanding.
(3) Laboratory techniques and manipulative devices should be used freely.

The report went on to stress the importance of well-prepared teachers for classes of slow learners. Teacher attitude is extremely important in working with these students, and care must be taken not to attach stigmas to the program. Enthusiasm, imagination, and understanding were all cited as important attitudes for a teacher to have.

Topics for inclusion in the curriculum were suggested which would provide motivation and help build prestige. Included were such items as elementary work with number bases, ancient methods of computation, indirect measurement, magic squares, experimental geometry, use of the slide rule, and a laboratory unit on probability and statistics. As guides in formulating an effective program, the following specific recommendations were made:

(1) A four-year sequence should be made available to all pupils in grades nine through twelve.
(2) Two years of mathematics should be required for graduation from all secondary schools.
(3) Where enrollment warrants, below-average pupils should be placed in separate classes, limited in size to a maximum of twenty pupils.
(4) It is the responsibility of the teacher to locate deficiencies and provide for remedial instruction within the classroom.
(5) If, at any time, a pupil shows sufficient growth and promise it should be possible for him to move into a program for more able pupils.

The committee concluded its report by stressing the need for a detailed outline, including specific resource units, for a four-year course of study in mathematics for below-average pupils. The NCTM was urged to take steps to meet this need and, as we shall see later in this chapter, acted accordingly.

2-2 SMSG Panel

In 1959 the School Mathematics Study Group (SMSG) formed a panel of educators and mathematicians to plan a program for students of average and below-average ability in mathematics. Sample text materials were prepared by writing groups during the summers of 1960, 1961, and 1962. These materials were tested in experimental centers throughout the country and have been made available for classroom use as follows:

Introduction to Secondary School Mathematics: a two-year program for grades 7 and 8 [34].
Introduction to Algebra: a two-year program for grades 9 and 10 [33].

The topics considered in these materials are essentially the same as those in the regular SMSG texts. The presentation of the topics differs in accord with the following guidelines which were used in the rewriting of the regular materials for students of average and below-average ability:

To adjust the reading level downward.
To shorten the chapters and to provide variation from chapter to chapter in terms of content.

To shorten sections within each chapter.
To introduce new concepts through the use of concrete examples.
To provide numerous illustrative examples.
To provide chapter summaries, chapter reviews, and cumulative sets of problems.

The authors of these texts for average and below-average students point out that the material is *not* offered as appropriate content for the very slow, non-college-bound student. Rather, it was hoped that the program would awaken the interest of students who may have unrecognized and undeveloped ability in mathematics, and whose progress may have been blocked through an inappropriate curriculum.

In experimental situations the texts entitled *Introduction to Secondary School Mathematics*, designed for average and below-average students in grades 7 and 8, have been successfully used with classes of very slow learners in grades 9 through 12 [37]. The results were gratifying, especially in terms of student interest in subject matter which, for the most part, they found to be new and exciting. Other materials are needed to obtain a similar new refreshing point of view among students who have had modern programs of mathematics in the elementary or junior high school grades.

In April, 1964, the SMSG held a "Conference on Mathematics Education for Below Average Achievers" to help determine what role the SMSG should play in this area. Recommendations were made and published as part of a conference report [32]. Throughout the discussion of culturally deprived groups, there was an emphasis upon the need for research data based upon the thesis that retardation in mental development is caused largely by deficient contact with physical and social environment in early years.

A major recommendation made was that material appealing to a variety of motivational interests and based on experiences of low-ability students should be prepared for use in grades K–12. Emphasis, however, should be on the mathematical principles involved in the applications. The assumptions made by some participants that the pupil of low ability should have a program founded on drill and should not be required to think was soundly rejected.

The importance of the teacher was evidenced by recommendations that a series of institutes be established which would deal specifically with the low-ability child, as well as with a study of suitable teaching techniques for such students.

2-3 U. S. Office of Education Conference

In cooperation with the NCTM, the U. S. Office of Education held a "Conference on the Low Achiever in Mathematics" in March, 1964, and published a preliminary and a final report that summarized the talks given and recommendations made [26], [38]. The conference dealt not only with the slow learner but also with all students in the lowest 30 percent based upon achievement in school mathematics.

One of the major recommendations made was that a National Commission on Mathematics Education for Low Achievers be established. Such a group could serve as a clearinghouse of promising practices in teaching mathematics to low achievers and could undertake such activities as publication of a yearbook, establishment of summer camps for low achievers, and establishment of lines of communication with industry, business, governmental agencies, and educational agencies.

It was suggested that research and development centers be established with extended research on such topics as the effectiveness of mathematics teachers who have been specially prepared to teach low achievers, the use of teacher assistants, and the value of such methods of teaching as the discovery approach. In-service programs for teachers of low achievers were cited as a major need, to be met by federally supported institutes as well as by consultant help.

The conference report concludes with an appendix that suggests guidelines in several areas. Administrative provisions include making available a course each year (K–12) for the low achiever, as well as providing for maximum individual growth through careful grouping. Stress was placed upon the role of the administrator in selecting teachers, competent both in subject matter and temperament, to teach the low achiever. An effective program must be based upon opportunities for intensive professional in-service education programs as well as for research and experimentation with new and different teaching techniques for low achievers in mathematics.

Since good instructional materials are sorely needed for below-average students, suggested guidelines for their preparation were also given. It was suggested that course content should be selected by a team of specialists from all areas with attention given to a new approach rather than to a slowed-down version of the program for the college-bound student as in the materials considered in §2-2. Emphasis was placed on the need for the low achiever to develop mathematical skills essential for gainful employment, with mathematical concepts to be learned through the use of models, audiovisual aids, and manipulative devices.

The guidelines prepared for teaching mathematics to the low achiever suggested the need once again for able and well-trained teachers who could exploit modern educational technology and provide experiences in the physical world. Classroom activities need to be purposeful and varied, and the low achiever must have his curiosity and imagination aroused through discovery exercises that are best presented in a laboratory setting.

The preliminary report of the conference [26] ends with the following inspirational message:

A teacher who accepts the fact that low achievers are teachable; a teacher who has a missionary spirit and a respect for the worth of pupils with limited ability; a teacher who is concerned and interested in individuals; a teacher who can make a pupil feel he not only belongs but also is important; a teacher who can instill a sense of worthiness, responsibility, and desire to achieve; a teacher who cares enough to give his very best to the low achievers will make the program a success.

2-4 National Council of Teachers of Mathematics

In 1962 the National Council of Teachers of Mathematics continued its vital interest in the problems of the slow learner and appointed a Committee on Mathematics for the Non-College Bound (MNCB). Funds were approved to finance a writing project to produce text materials for ninth grade students in the 25th to 50th percentile range in mathematics achievement.

The committee decided that it was essential to provide opportunities for genuine mathematical discovery at the maturity level of the students to motivate further study of mathematics. Units were to be developed that would be as independent of each other as possible, and that would not depend upon a prolonged systematic development. New topics were to be developed, rather than a mere review of old topics. Specifically, the content should extend student appreciation and understanding of principles in the area of number, operation, measurement and approximation, function and relation, proof, symbolic representation, probability and selections, and problem solving [31].

In the summer of 1963 a preliminary text, *Experiences in Mathematical Discovery*, was written; it was tested in various classrooms throughout the United States during the school year 1963–64. These preliminary materials led to ten individual units published by the NCTM [25], under the following titles:

(1) Formulas, Graphs, and Patterns
(2) Properties of Operations with Numbers
(3) Mathematical Sentences
(4) Geometry
(5) Arrangements and Selections
(6) Mathematical Thinking
(7) Rational Numbers
(8) Ratios, Proportion, and Percent
(9) Measurement
(10) Positive and Negative Numbers

Any one or more of the aforementioned units may be used by teachers to explore the use of a discovery approach, with class discussion exercises provided in the texts as the major means of presenting basic concepts. Exposition as such is kept to a minimum; the student is led to discover and verbalize ideas by himself, although basic mathematical concepts are formulated for each unit.

The NCTM does not wish to enter the textbook publishing business. Rather, it hopes that these units will provide the necessary stimulus for the publication of a wide variety of commercial materials for low achievers that are original and stimulating in point of view and presentation. The NCTM's interest in all students, and in particular the average and below average, is continuing with plans for a future yearbook on teaching the slow learner. Also, the NCTM is conducting extensive discussions of ways of developing instructional systems (films, film strips, programmed materials, special text materials, etc.) to meet the special needs of these students.

2-5 Summary

The outlook for the future is brightening. At long last the mathematical community is becoming aware of the fact that we must provide an adequate program of mathematics for all students, including those of average and below-average ability. If we expect to maintain the progress of our civilization, we simply need to develop this huge source of manpower. Help is on the way, and the mathematics teacher can soon look forward to receiving aid from various sources.

On the other hand, teachers are still faced with the day-by-day task of providing for the slow learner until suitable published materials are available. The remainder of this text will be devoted to an exploration of specific units of study that have proved to be successful with groups of slow learners. These topics have been designed to motivate the learning of mathematics and to reawaken some of the latent interest of the low achiever.

Questions for Discussion

1. Several writers have indicated that one of the causes of low achievement seems to be "poverty of experience." Discuss this phrase and prepare arguments to support or refute the assertion made.
2. Examine the SMSG text *Introduction to Secondary School Mathematics* and compare it with their two-volume sequence entitled *Mathematics for Junior High School.*
3. Read and compare the reports of the conferences held by SMSG and the U. S. Office of Education in terms of objectives, scope, and outcomes.
4. Most groups urge that full use be made of audiovisual aids in the teaching of mathematics to slow learners. Discuss various aids that might be

used and illustrate their use in teaching specific topics that are suitable for such students.

5. Indicate some of the steps that you, as an administrator, might take to see that order is maintained in the classrooms of low achievers.
6. The U. S. Office of Education suggested that special college or in-service courses be offered in the teaching of mathematics to low achievers. Outline the contents that might be included in such a course which would meet for fifteen two-hour sessions.

chapter 3

Explorations with Numbers and Numerals

This chapter is the first of a set of chapters that deal with suggested topics to be used at various grade levels with slow learners. These are to be considered as resource units for teachers to use to motivate learning and stimulate the imaginations of this group of students. Some of the suggestions are for topics that can be developed in fifteen minutes, whereas others lend themselves to two- or three-week units. In each case our aim is to provide sources of ideas that teachers can adapt to their individual class situations.

3-1 Estimations

Effective teachers provide frequent and numerous opportunities for students to make discoveries and explorations on their own. One of the great joys of the study of mathematics is that of making such explorations, a joy seldom appreciated by the slow learner only because of lack of suitable opportunities. The following questions involving the estimation of answers are of a type that generally stimulate a great deal of interest on the part of all learners. Approximate answers should be given before any measurements or computations are made.

(1) How long would it take to count to a million at the rate of one number per second if you were to continue without stopping?

In the class discussion don't accept the answer of one million seconds! Ask how long this is in terms of hours, days, weeks, months, or years. Answers will vary greatly (even among adults). This variation can be capitalized upon to explore means of actually computing the answer, thus providing a highly motivated setting for a review of some of the fundamentals of arithmetic. Notice also that this concept of large numbers is an important one to discuss in today's society.

(2) How high would a stack of one million pennies reach? Would it go up to the ceiling? Would it reach over the school building? Would it be higher than the Empire State Building?

Here again random guesses and discussion should be encouraged. This can then lead to a discussion of measurement and to exploration of means of attaining the correct answer to the problem through such questions as: How would you find the thickness of one penny? Of ten pennies?

There are many other questions of the type we have just considered. Some of these are listed below. In each case, estimation of answers and discussion of procedures for obtaining approximate answers should precede formal computation.

(3) How much would a million pennies weigh?
(4) If a million dollar bills were placed end to end in a straight line, approximately, how far would they reach?
(5) How many coins are there in a pound of nickels?
(6) Many centuries ago the distance from a person's elbow to the tip of his outstretched fingers, (that is, one cubit) was used as a unit of measure. What is the length of your classroom in cubits? What are some of the disadvantages of this unit of measure?
(7) Approximately how many basketballs could be placed in your classroom if all the furniture were removed and every bit of space utilized?
(8) How many standard postal cards would be needed, placed end to end, to completely encircle the globe at the equator?

These questions are illustrative of only one type that can be created to involve each student with estimations, counting, and measurement. Such questions may be presented as a unit of work or merely used on occasion as an attention-gaining device. As indicated earlier, they prove to be an interesting way of motivating a review of the fundamentals of arithmetic and a discussion of large numbers.

3-2 Number Patterns

A search for patterns lends excitement to the mathematics classroom and often leads to a discovery. Slow learners can be led to make discoveries by searching for arithmetic patterns that exist in a variety of situations. Gradually many students begin to wonder why such patterns appear. This provides a basis for presenting important concepts in a highly motivated setting.

One very simple example that most students never have had called to their attention is the pattern associated with the multiples of nine.

Consider the sequence of the products 9, 18, . . . , 90; in each case the sum of the digits is 9. Consider the sequence of the units digits, and of the tens digits. What is the pattern that you see? In each case the student should be led to search for an explanation of the pattern and to explore the manner in which it continues for other integral multiples of 9.

$$\begin{aligned} 1 \times 9 &= 9 \\ 2 \times 9 &= 18 \\ 3 \times 9 &= 27 \\ 4 \times 9 &= 36 \\ 5 \times 9 &= 45 \\ 6 \times 9 &= 54 \\ 7 \times 9 &= 63 \\ 8 \times 9 &= 72 \\ 9 \times 9 &= 81 \\ 10 \times 9 &= 90 \end{aligned}$$

One historical anecdote that involves a pattern concerns the story of the mathematician Gauss (1777–1855). At an early age he was reported to have found the sum of the numbers from 1 through 100 as follows:

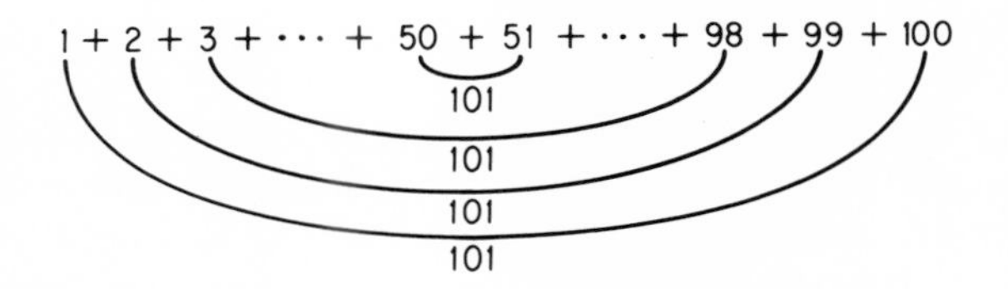

There are 50 pairs of numbers, each with a sum of 101. Thus the total sum is 50×101 or 5050.

Average and below-average students find special pleasure in such mental gymnastics. Many other sums such as the following can be suggested:

$$1 + 2 + 3 + \cdots + 50$$
$$2 + 4 + 6 + \cdots + 100$$

Be sure that you have an even number of addends, or help the students see the special role of the middle number when there are an odd number of addends.

We are concerned with the joy of discovery; we are not concerned with formal proofs. As an example of this distinction, consider this sequence of pairs of expressions:

$$\begin{array}{ll} 1 + 3 & 2 \times 2 \\ 1 + 3 + 5 & 3 \times 3 \\ 1 + 3 + 5 + 7 & 4 \times 4 \end{array}$$

Be sure that you see the pattern between the sums in the left-hand column and the products in the right-hand column. Write down the next two pairs of expressions in this pattern. Describe the expressions on the left in words. Find a relationship between each expression on the left and its corresponding expression on the right. If you have actually followed these directions, you should understand the manner in which such pairs of expressions can be used to lead students to the "discovery" that the sum of the first n odd integers is equal to n^2. Such discoveries can be very meaningful to students. The teacher serves as the "authority" and no further proofs are needed at this time, especially for students of average and below-average ability. There is a place in the curriculum for formal proofs, but these should not be allowed to dull the joys of discovery.

Two other patterns will be mentioned in this section; many others can be developed. Our next number pattern may be represented by this sequence of expressions:

$$\frac{1}{1\cdot 2}$$

$$\frac{1}{1\cdot 2}+\frac{1}{2\cdot 3}$$

$$\frac{1}{1\cdot 2}+\frac{1}{2\cdot 3}+\frac{1}{3\cdot 4}$$

Notice that the value of the first expression is $\frac{1}{2}$, the value of the second one is $\frac{2}{3}$, and the value of the third expression is $\frac{3}{4}$.

By finding the value of each of the preceding expressions, students can be led to "discover" that the sum of the following is $\frac{9}{10}$:

$$\frac{1}{1\cdot 2}+\frac{1}{2\cdot 3}+\frac{1}{3\cdot 4}+\cdots+\frac{1}{9\cdot 10}$$

After this, the student can be asked to use his discovery and find the following sum:

$$\frac{1}{1\cdot 2}+\frac{1}{2\cdot 3}+\frac{1}{3\cdot 4}+\cdots+\frac{1}{99\cdot 100}$$

Our final number pattern involves a triangular array that is representative of many such patterns available in the literature [12].

$$\begin{aligned}
1 &= 1\\
1+2+1 &= 4\\
1+2+3+2+1 &= 9\\
1+2+3+4+3+2+1 &= 16
\end{aligned}$$

This should lead to the following discovery:

$$1+2+3+\cdots+n+\cdots+3+2+1=n^2$$

3-3 Numerals Base Five

A unit on other systems of numeration was originally incorporated into the mathematics curriculum as a topic for the advanced student. This topic is also quite appropriate for the slow learner when presented in an interesting manner without undue emphasis on mechanical operations. It provides another opportunity for a review of the fundamentals of arithmetic in disguised form and has proved to be an effective topic for stimulating interest. Here are three possible ways to begin a unit on a base five system of numeration.

Imagine that our monetary system of coins consisted only of pennies, nickels, and quarters. Then complete the following table showing how to obtain the sums listed using the fewest number of coins possible.

Amount	25¢	5¢	1¢
67¢			
34¢			
23¢			
82¢			

Now consider the amount needed to obtain 82¢: 3 quarters, 1 nickel, and 2 pennies. Let us agree to write this as 312_M, where the M means that the numeral is in terms of our special monetary system. Then, for example, 234_M means 2 quarters, 3 nickels, and 4 pennies, or 69¢.

This approach is based upon concrete aspects of the students' experience and can provide an effective basis for the study of the base five system of notation. Here is another approach.

Assume that the base number is 5. You are then required to obtain a given number, say 44, by placing marks in a box where each mark stands for 1, 5, or 25, depending upon the column in which it is placed.

Base number: 5

44:

25	5	1
I	III	IIII

If the base number is 6, then the columns are headed 1, 6, and 36; for 7 they are headed 1, 7, and 49. Here are two more examples:

Base number: 6

80:

36	6	1
//	/	//

Base number: 7

162:

49	7	1
///	//	/

This approach can be used when the base number is any positive integer n greater than 1 and with as many columns as you wish headed $1, n, n^2, n^3, n^4$, ... Extensive arithmetical practice can be provided in this way. To win the game the player must obtain the number given by using the fewest number of possible marks.

Our final approach is for the imaginative teacher who can tell the class of his recent visit to Mars where the underground inhabitants have only one hand and thus count by fingers and hands as follows:

0, 1, 2, 3, 4, hand
hand and 1, hand and 2, hand and 3, hand and 4, 2 hands
2 hands and 1, 2 hands and 2, . . .

The discussion of writing symbols for numbers can lead to the usual place value base five system of notation:

$0, 1, 2, 3, 4, 10_{\text{five}}$
$11_{\text{five}}, 12_{\text{five}}, 13_{\text{five}}, 14_{\text{five}}, 20_{\text{five}}$
$21_{\text{five}}, 22_{\text{five}}, \ldots$

The student should now be given opportunities to complete simple exercises in grouping. For example, to write a base five numeral for the following collection of marks, he would group by fives as indicated.

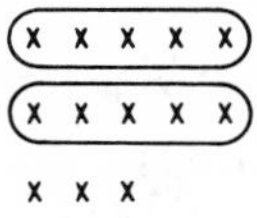

x x x x x
x x x x x
x x x

$13 = 2 \text{ fives} + 3 \text{ ones}$
$= 23_{\text{five}}$

Other number bases may be introduced by grouping the same collection of marks by some other number, such as six:

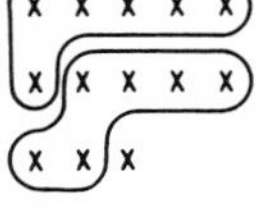

x x x x x
x x x x x
x x x

$13 = 2 \text{ sixes} + 1 \text{ one}$
$= 21_{\text{six}}$

The types of skills and concepts that one can reasonably expect to develop with slow learners are illustrated by these examples:

(1) Write 213_{five} as a base ten numeral.
(2) Write 63 in base five notation.
(3) Add: $123_{\text{five}} + 214_{\text{five}}$.
(4) Multiply: $3_{\text{five}} \times 24_{\text{five}}$.

It is not usually worthwhile to try to develop skills beyond these. For slow learners, a unit on numeration should be presented primarily to create interest, to provide additional practice in the fundamentals of arithmetic, and to develop an appreciation of our own decimal system of numeration.

Some teachers have considered other skills and concepts. A few have even been able to relate the pattern of multiples of 9 in base ten (§3-2) to multiples of $n - 1$ in base n. For example, the multiples of 6 in base seven numeration are as follows:

$1 \times 6 = 6$
$2 \times 6 = 15_{\text{seven}}$
$3 \times 6 = 24_{\text{seven}}$
$4 \times 6 = 33_{\text{seven}}$
$5 \times 6 = 42_{\text{seven}}$
$6 \times 6 = 51_{\text{seven}}$

The sum of the digits in each case is 6. The units digits decrease (6, 5, 4, 3, 2, 1) whereas the digits representing sevens increase from 0 through 5.

3-4 Early Egyptian Numerals

The systems of numeration used by early civilizations are often interesting. We shall consider, as an example, the Egyptian hieroglyphic system of notation. The following symbols are used:

1	|	vertical stroke
10	∩	heel bone
100	9	coil of rope
1000	𓆼	lotus flower
10,000	𓂭	pointed finger

This system has a base of ten, but has no place value. For example, ∩||, ||∩, and |∩| all represent one ten and two ones, or twelve. Here are some decimal numerals written in this notation:

123 = 9∩∩|||

13,241 = 𓂭𓆼𓆼𓆼99∩∩∩∩|

Students will enjoy computing in this system and should profit in terms of an increased understanding of some of the basic ideas of borrowing and carrying. The following examples will illustrate this:

Addition: 36 + 27

∩∩∩|||||| + ∩∩||||||| (carry ∩)

∩∩∩||| + ∩∩

sum = ∩∩∩∩∩∩||| = 63

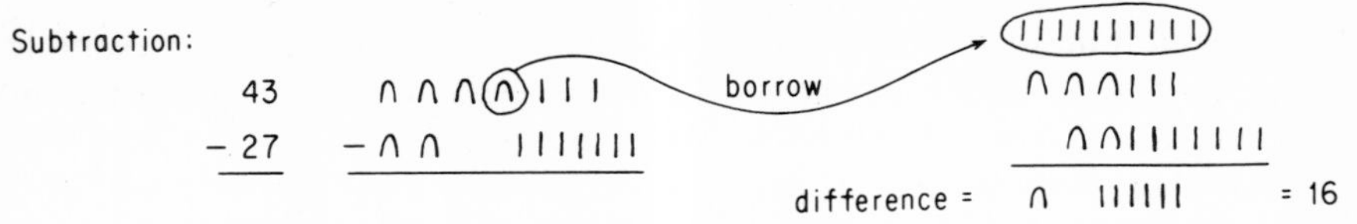

Exploration of other systems of numeration (Babylonian, Greek, etc.) may prove of interest to some students but should not ordinarily be considered in detail. A study of Roman numerals, and especially the relation of this system of notation to the construction of an abacus, can be particularly worthwhile [10].

3-5 Explorations with Binary Notation

There are several very interesting experiments based upon the principles of binary notation. Some of these may be performed profitably by slow learners even though the intricacies of a base two system of notation may prove to be too complex for them.

Our first experiment requires a set of cards to be used in a mind-reading game. The numbers 1 through 15 are first written in base two notation as follows:

Base 10	*Base 2*	*Base 10*	*Base 2*
1	1	9	1001
2	10	10	1010
3	11	11	1011
4	100	12	1100
5	101	13	1101
6	110	14	1110
7	111	15	1111
8	1000		

Four cards *A*, *B*, *C*, and *D* are needed. On card *A* we list all numbers that have a 1 in the units place when written in binary notation as in the figure. (Note that these will be all of the odd numbers from 1 through 15.) On card *B* we list all numbers with a 1 in the second position from the right in binary notation. On card *C* we list all numbers with a 1 in the third position, and on card *D* we list all numbers with a 1 in the fourth position.

To play the game you ask someone to think of a number and tell you in which box or boxes it appears. You then tell that person his number by

A	*B*	*C*	*D*
1	2	4	8
3	3	5	9
5	6	6	10
7	7	7	11
9	10	12	12
11	11	13	13
13	14	14	14
15	15	15	15

finding the sum of the first number in each box he mentions. For example, if his number is 11, he lists boxes *A*, *B*, and *D*. You are then able to find the sum $1 + 2 + 8$ as the number under discussion.

Another worthwhile classroom experiment is the construction of a series of punched cards that shows how the binary system of notation may be used in the process of card sorting. First prepare a set of sixteen index cards with four holes punched in each and a corner notched as in the accompanying figure. Next represent the numbers 0 through 15 on these cards in binary notation. Cut out the space above each hole to represent 1; leave the hole untouched to represent 0. Several cards are shown in the figure.

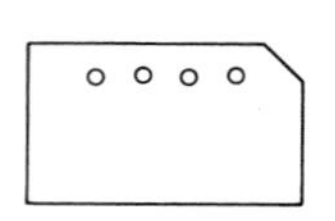

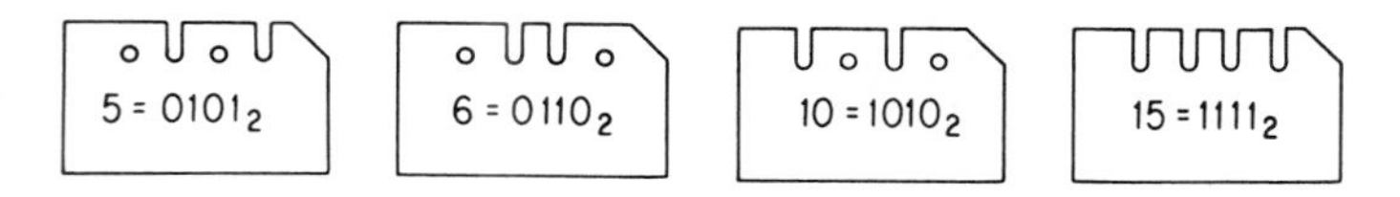

After all the cards have been completed in this manner, shuffle them thoroughly and align them, making certain that they remain "face up." (The notched corners will help indicate when the cards are right side up.) Then, going from right to left, perform the following operation: Stick a pencil or other similar object through the first hole and lift up. Some of the cards will come up, namely those in which the holes have not been cut through to the edge of the card (that is, those cards representing numbers whose units digit in binary notation is 0).

Place the cards that lift up in front of the other cards and repeat the same operation for the remaining holes in order from right to left. When you have finished, the cards should be in numerical order, 0 through 15.

Note that only four operations are needed to arrange the sixteen cards. As the number of cards is doubled, only one additional operation is needed to place them in order. That is, 32 cards may be placed in numerical order with five of the described card-sorting operations, 64 cards may be arranged with six operations, 128 cards with seven operations, and so forth. Thus a large number of cards may be arranged in order with a relatively small number of operations. For example, over one billion cards may be placed in numerical order with only thirty sortings.

3-6 Summary

Explorations with numbers and numerals are particularly well-suited for use with the slow learner inasmuch as they relate quite closely with his past mathematical experiences. The ability to make reasonable estimations is an important one to develop, and this can be done quite effectively through the use of questions of the type considered in §3-1.

Although originally included in the curriculum for above-average students, numerous experiments have provided evidence that slow learners can profit from an exposure to work with nondecimal systems of numeration. Such work provides a welcome relief from routine computational drill, while at the same time it offers a basis for a better understanding of our own base ten system of numeration. For an introduction to other number bases written for students of average and below-average ability in the junior high school, see [34]. This text has also been successfully used with classes of very slow learners in grades 9 through 12 [37]. A unit on number systems appears in [16]. Copies of this booklet may be obtained free of charge, in classroom quantities, from the Institute of Life Insurance, 277 Park Avenue, New York, 10017. For additional background information on systems of numeration see [22] and [23]. A book on the history of mathematics, such as [5], is another good source of information on ancient systems of numeration.

Questions for Discussion

1. Estimate and then find approximate answers for each of the questions suggested in §3-1.
2. Develop a set of five additional questions that involve estimation and measurement, similar to those in §3-1.
3. Consider the following pattern:

$$\frac{1}{1\cdot 2} = \frac{1}{1} - \frac{1}{2}; \quad \frac{1}{2\cdot 3} = \frac{1}{2} - \frac{1}{3}; \quad \cdots \frac{1}{9\cdot 10} = \frac{1}{9} - \frac{1}{10}$$

Use this pattern to provide an explanation for the value of the series

$$\frac{1}{1\cdot 2} + \frac{1}{2\cdot 3} + \frac{1}{3\cdot 4} + \cdots + \frac{1}{9\cdot 10}$$

4. Extend the mind-reading game described in §3-5 to include the numbers 1 through 31. (A fifth card E will be necessary.)
5. Extend the procedure described in §3-5 to construct punched cards for the numbers 0 through 31.
6. Prepare a five-day unit of study on other systems of numeration for use in a class of very slow students. If possible, teach the unit at two different levels such as in grades 9 and 12. Evaluate the results in terms of student achievement, participation, and interest.
7. Find a reference such as [20] to the game of Nim and describe the relationship of the game to the binary system of notation.

chapter 4

Explorations with Geometric Figures

There are numerous interesting and exciting side roads in geometry that may be explored with slow learners and that also have educational values for them. Frequently, slow learners find this aspect of mathematics somewhat more appealing because of its concrete nature. Once again, however, emphasis needs to be placed on the laboratory-discovery type of approach wherever possible. The following topics have been successfully used and are presented as examples of fruitful explorations with geometric figures.

4-1 Optical Illusions

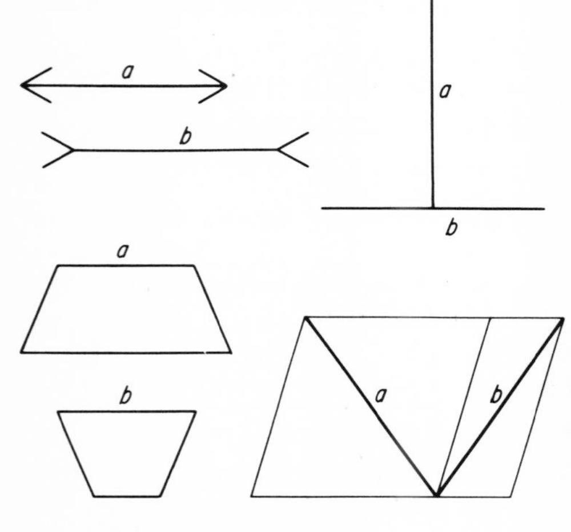

Optical illusions are always of interest to slow learners. Examples of optical illusions may be presented as an integral part of a lesson; they may also be used in bulletin-board displays. In each case they provide a means of convincing the student that one cannot rely solely on intuition or visualization. In this set of four figures, each of the figures includes two line segments, *a* and *b*. Which of the segments appears to be the larger?

In each of the next three figures see whether you can guess which line segments, if any, are parallel. You should have found, in both cases, that

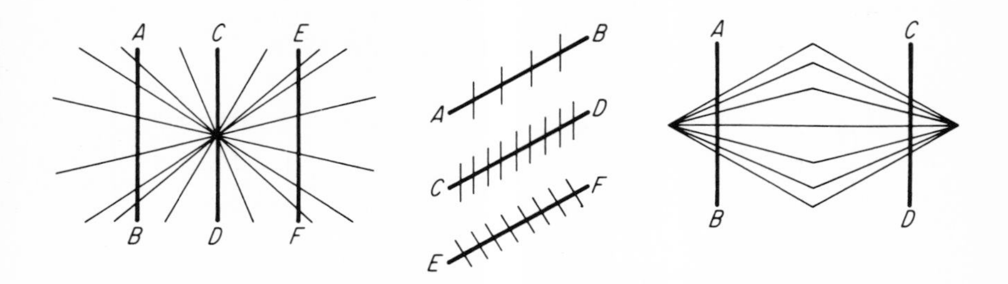

looks can be deceiving. In each of the first four drawings, the segments are equal in length; in each of the last three they are parallel!

The next figure provides an optical illusion that was recently created and that is most startling at first glance. It really requires no explanation. Place a copy of the figure on the bulletin board, and watch the expressions of the students and the ensuing interest in a study of geometry.

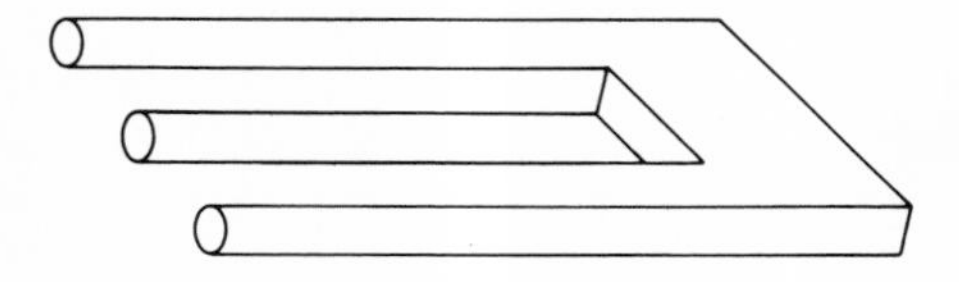

4-2 Geometric Patterns

Many interesting classroom activities which include geometric patterns can be prepared for slow learners. Consider these figures for which the student is to discover a pattern and then use his discovery to complete the picture.

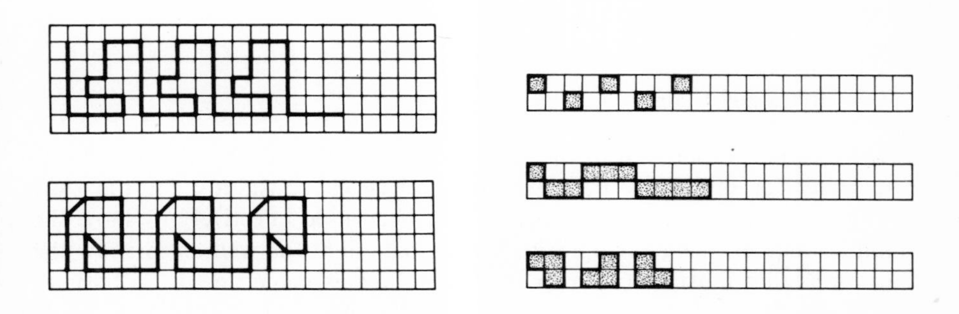

Another interesting exploration with geometric patterns involves the discovery of various arrangements that can be made with sets of squares that are joined along their edges. In general, these figures are referred to as **polyominoes.**

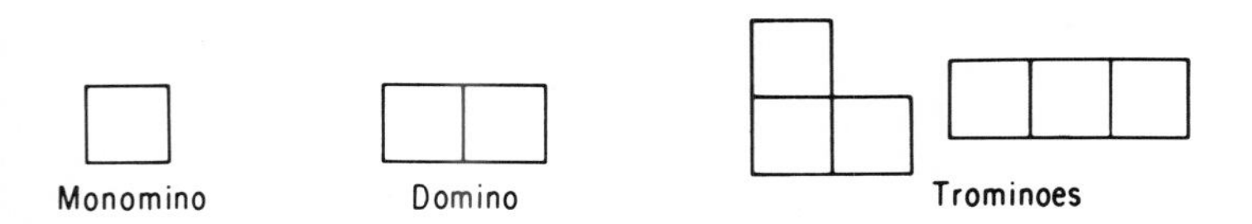

A single square, a **monomino,** can be arranged in only one way as shown. Two squares, a **domino,** can also be arranged in only one way since the position of the 2×1 rectangle does not affect the arrangement. That is, any two such figures are congruent. There are two distinct arrangements for a **tromino,** that is, three squares.

Next consider a **tetromino,** a set of four squares. Here we find that there are five possible arrangements such that no two are congruent. Thus, as in the case of the domino and other arrangements, we exclude any rearrangement that merely consists of a rotation which places the same squares in a congruent position. The five possible arrangements are shown in the figure.

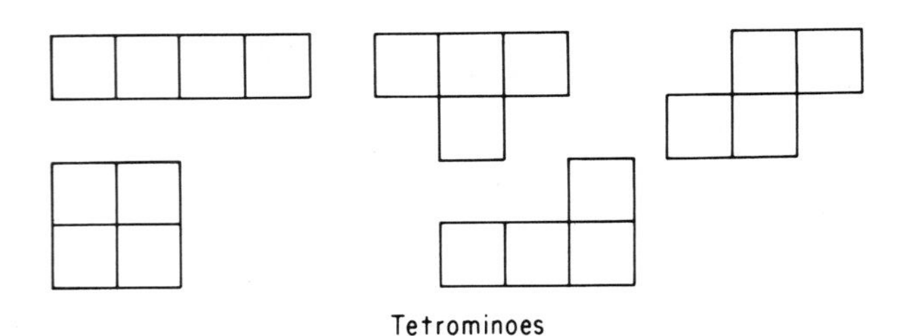

Through the use of graph paper, or small square objects, slow learners can explore such arrangements and use these as a basis for further studies of geometric figures.

4-3 Circles and Chords

The discovery approach to the learning of mathematics, or more precisely, teaching for discovery, needs to be emphasized constantly for the slow learner. The following explorations have been used effectively to show the importance of using examples to make predictions, as well as to show the cautions that must be taken to verify conclusions made on such a basis.

Consider a circle and a chord of the circle. This chord divides the circle into two regions. With two chords, four regions are obtained. Let us see if a pattern can be found concerning the *maximum* number of regions that exist as additional chords are drawn:

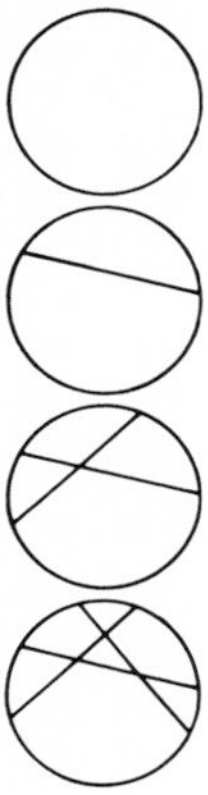

Figure	Number of chords	Number of regions	Increase in number of regions
	0	1	
			+1
	1	2	
			+2
	2	4	
			+3
	3	7	

Note the pattern of number of regions and the manner in which they increase. For three chords it appears that we should have $4 + 3$ or 7 regions. Let the student conjecture the number of regions for four chords from this pattern and confirm his conjecture by experimentation.

Now consider the following set of figures for another exploration.

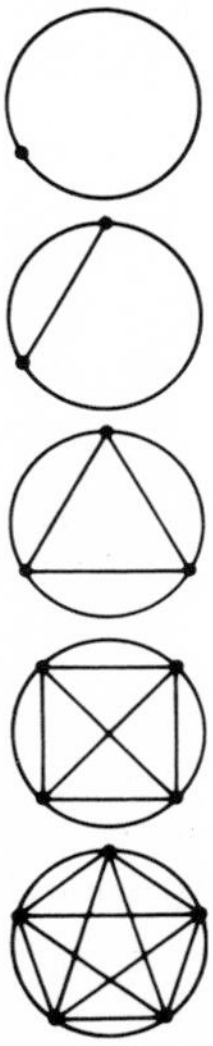

Figure	Number of points	Number of chords	Number of regions
	1	0	1
	2	1	2
	3	3	4
	4	6	8
	5	10	16

This is another exploration (see figure at bottom of preceding page) including circles and chords. Consider the maximum number of regions into which a circle can be divided if the points on the circle are connected in all possible ways.

As each new point is added, the number of regions is doubled. Thus for six points, one would normally expect to find 32 regions. Let your students attempt to verify this conjecture by actual construction. Unfortunately, the pattern fails at this point; there are only 31 regions. But this teaches an important concept—patterns lead to conjectures, but these need to be confirmed.

4-4 Cubes and Spheres

Ask your students to picture a three-inch cube that is painted red. Now let us assume that we are to divide this cube into 27 one-inch cubes as in the figure. How many of these one-inch cubes will have red paint on none of its faces? On one face only? On two faces only? On three faces only? On more than three faces?

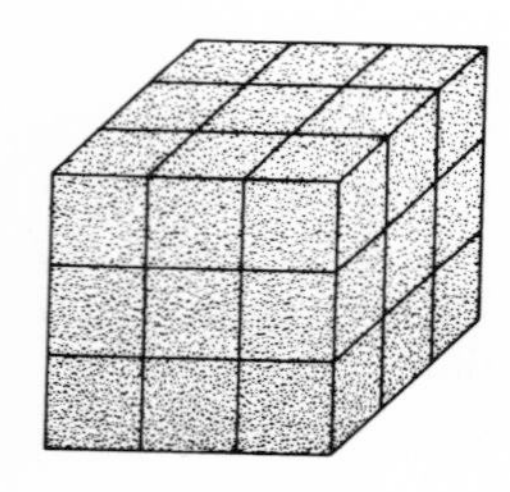

Spatial perception is an important skill that we try to develop in mathematics. Explorations such as the one we have just considered for a three-inch cube can be used effectively. If your students cannot visualize this figure on the basis of a plane drawing, then have them build a figure using blocks, sugar cubes, etc. For those who care to continue, try to answer the same questions for a four-inch cube.

Another exploration to develop spatial visualization can be based upon these questions:

(1) What is the maximum number of pieces that can be obtained by slicing an orange with two cuts?
(2) What is the maximum number if three cuts are to be made? (The pieces need not be of the same size.)
(3) What is the maximum number if four cuts are to be made? (This is an interesting but far more difficult question to answer.)

4-5 Patterns for Models

Students can learn many geometric facts as well as develop spatial abilities by constructing models of some of the common geometric solids. The patterns for these solids should first be drawn on graph paper or be prepared in advance by the teacher for those students of very low ability level. Here are the patterns for two common solids:

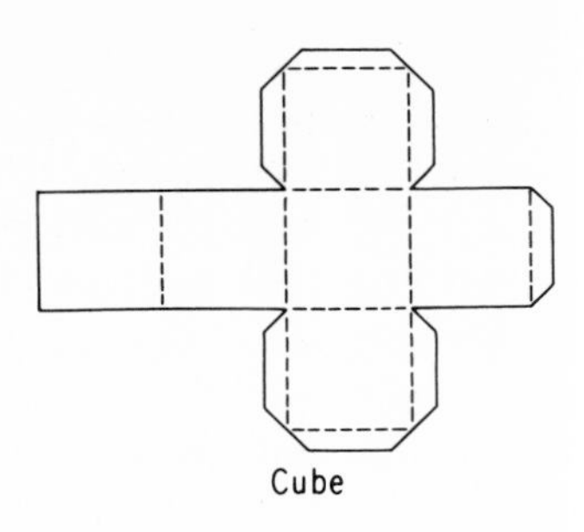

Cube

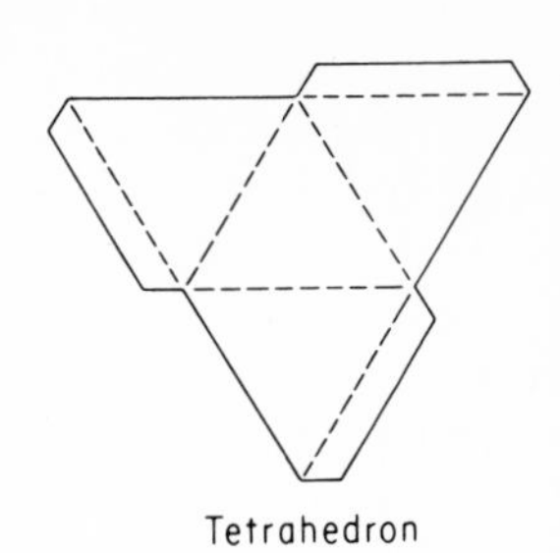

Tetrahedron

After constructing several models, or with the use of teacher-constructed models, you can lead students to discover **Euler's formula,** $V + F - E = 2$. This formula states that the number, V, of vertices plus the number, F, of faces is two more than the number, E, of edges. For example:

	V	F	E	$V+F-E$
Cube	8	6	12	2
Tetrahedron	4	4	6	2
Square pyramid	5	5	8	2

An interesting analogy can be made if we show the application of a modification of Euler's formula to figures on a plane. In this case consider the number V of vertices, the number A of arcs, the number R of regions, and the expression $V + R - A$. A square, for example, has 4 vertices, 4 arcs, and divides the plane into 2 regions (inside and outside of the square).

V	R	A	$V+R-A$
4	2	4	2
4	3	5	2
5	5	8	2
10	7	15	2

4-6 Paper Folding

Many interesting geometric concepts can be developed intuitively through the media of paper folding. Here is an example of the sort of exploration that can be made. Waxed paper is very useful for this kind of project.

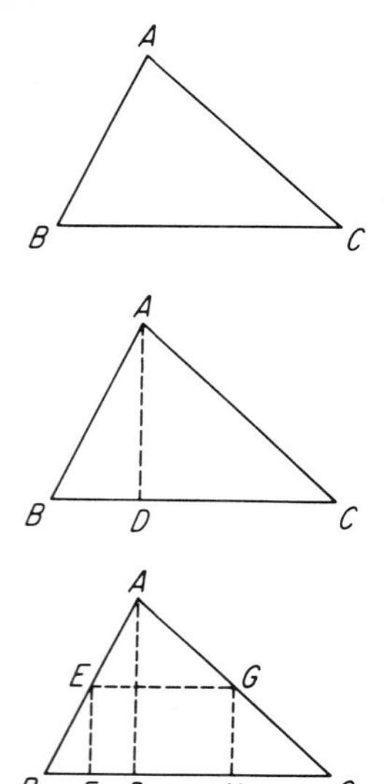

(1) Cut out a triangular region *ABC*.
(2) Fold the point *B* onto the line segment *BC* so that the crease $\overline{AD}$ passes through *A*. This determines the point *D* on $\overline{BC}$.
(3) Fold *B* over to *D*, forming the crease *EF*, as in the figure.
(4) Fold *C* over to *D*, forming the crease *GH*, as in the figure.
(5) Fold *A* down to *D*, forming the crease *EG*.

Now notice that when all three points *A*, *B*, and *C* are folded over to the point *D*, the angles at *A*, *B*, and *C* appear to form an angle of 180°.

Notice also that the length of $\overline{EG}$, the line segment joining the midpoints of two sides of $\triangle ABC$, is equal to the length of $\overline{FH}$. Also, since $\overline{BF} \cong \overline{FD}$ and $\overline{DH} \cong \overline{HC}$, the length of $\overline{EG}$ is one-half the length of $\overline{BC}$. Thus we have a demonstration of the fact that the line segment joining the midpoints of two sides of a triangle is equal in length to one-half the third side of the triangle.

Paper folding can be used to show many algebraic relationships as well as geometric ones. We shall consider two such examples here.

Example 1

(1) Take a square sheet of paper, *ABCD*.
(2) Fold $\overline{DC}$ onto $\overline{AB}$ forming the crease $\overline{EF}$.

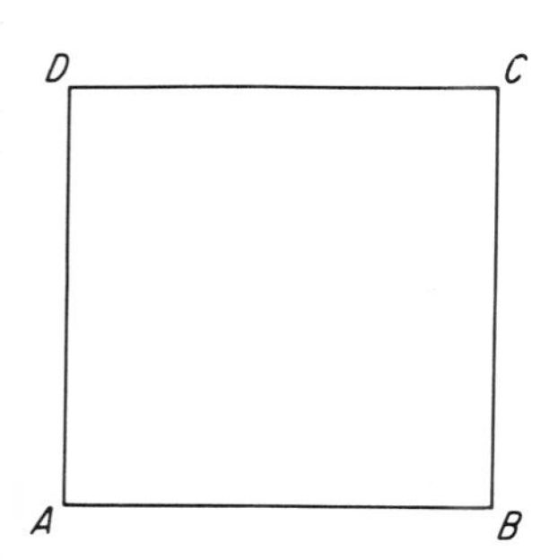

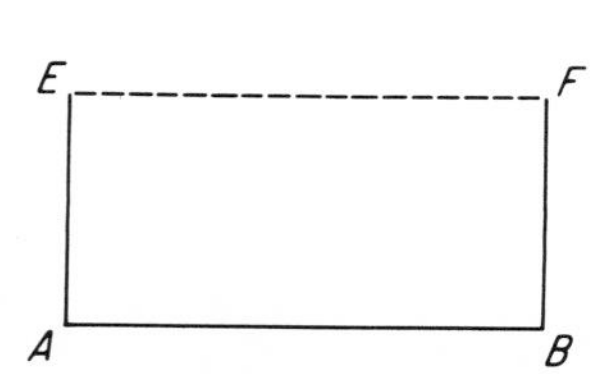

(3) Fold $\overline{BF}$ onto $\overline{AE}$ forming the crease $\overline{GH}$.
(4) If $\overline{AH}$ has length x, then each side of square $AHGE$ has length x, and the square has area x^2.
(5) If we unfold $\overline{BF}$ from $\overline{AE}$, then $\overline{AB}$ has length $2x$ and rectangle $ABFE$ has area $x^2 + x^2$, that is, $2x^2$.

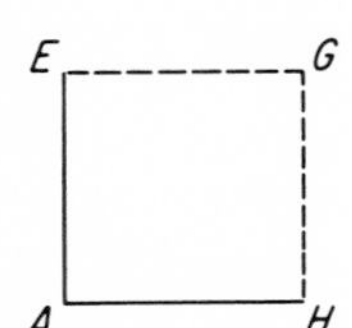

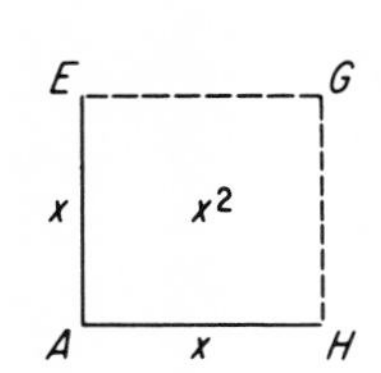

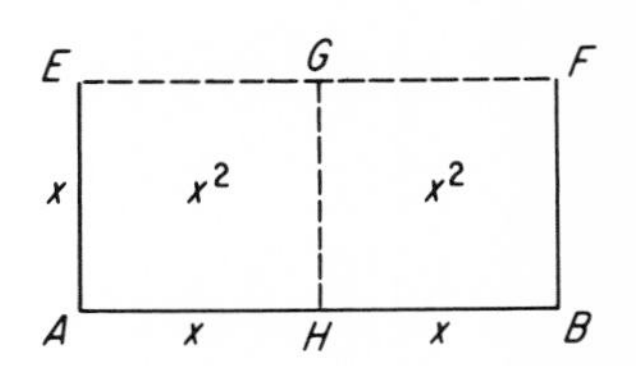

(6) If we unfold $\overline{DC}$ from $\overline{AB}$, then $\overline{BC}$ has length $2x$, and square $ABCD$ has area $(2x)^2$, that is, $4x^2$. This model can be used to help students distinguish between $2x^2$ and $(2x)^2$.

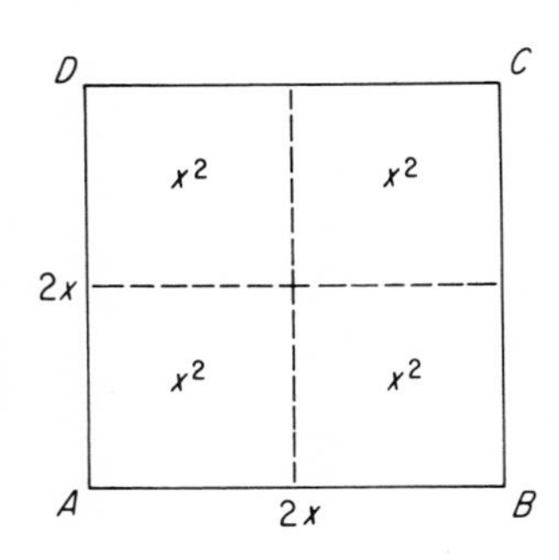

Example 2 Our second example of a geometric approach to algebra provides a model for the statement:

$$a^2 - b^2 = (a - b)(a + b)$$

(1) Start with a square sheet of paper, $PQRS$, with side a and area a^2.
(2) Fold the sheet along the diagonal $\overline{PR}$.
(3) Fold the point P a short distance b onto $\overline{PS}$, as in the figure, forming a crease $\overline{MN}$. Then cut the paper along this crease.

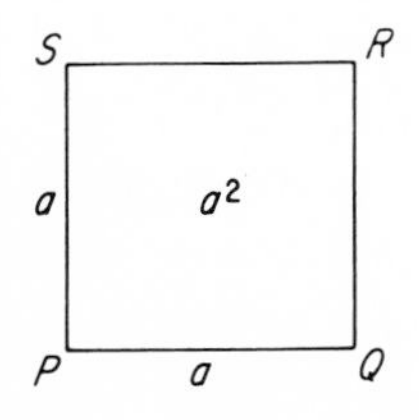

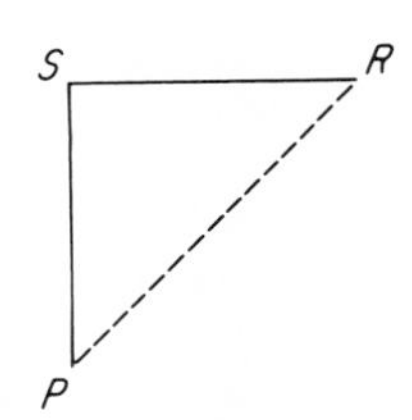

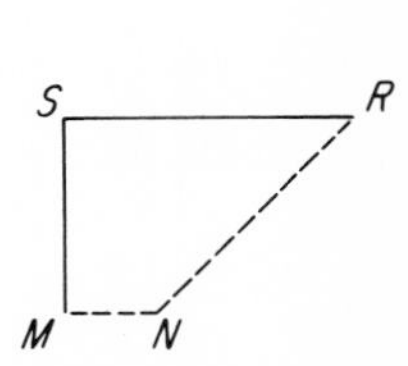

(4) Next unfold the sheet of paper. This remaining sheet has area $a^2 - b^2$.
(5) Cut along line segment NR.
(6) Rearrange the two parts to form a rectangle with dimensions $a + b$ and $a - b$. This rectangle has area $(a - b)(a + b)$. Since the total area of the two pieces does not depend upon the position of the pieces, the last two figures have the same area. That is,

$$a^2 - b^2 = (a - b)(a + b)$$

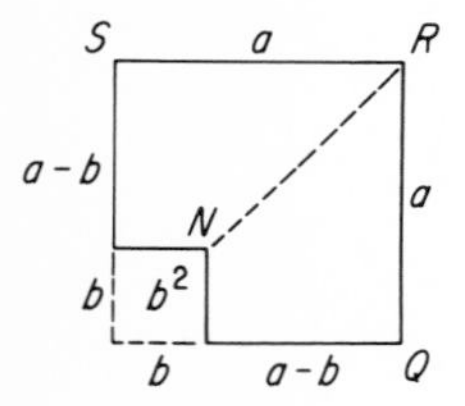

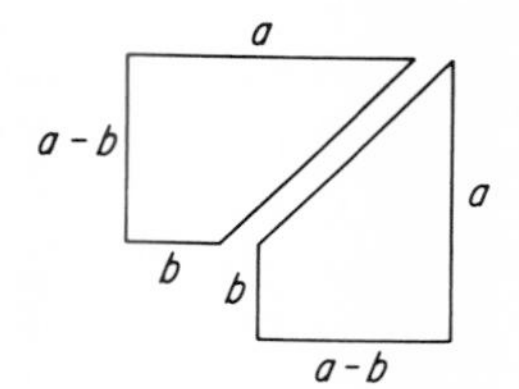

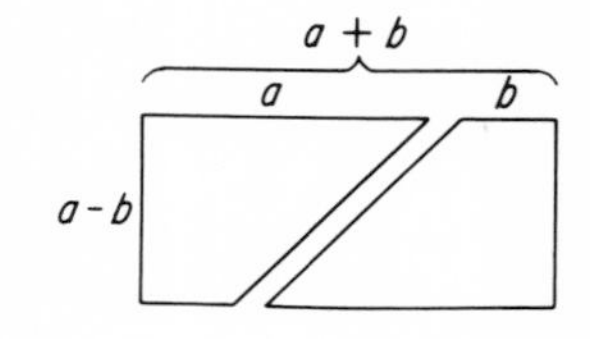

4-7 Summary

Many slow learners enjoy working with geometric figures and find such explorations to be far more concrete and meaningful than topics in arithmetic. They provide an opportunity for the student to become actively involved in the subject and to make use of whatever creative abilities he may have. However, it must constantly be emphasized that such material is of value and interest only if approached through an emphasis on discovery in a laboratory-type approach.

The teacher who wishes to find an extensive discussion of polyominoes may do so in [8]. An excellent presentation of many techniques of paper folding appears in [18]. For other geometric patterns, the teacher would do well to begin a collection of such items since they are not readily available in any one source.

Questions for Discussion

1. Prepare a bulletin-board display on optical illusions. Find as many as you can other than those presented in this chapter.
2. Develop a set of ten patterns similar to those considered in §4-2. Use your patterns with a group of slow learners and report on the results.
3. Extend the procedures considered in §4-2, and see how many arrangements you can form with five squares. There are twelve such pentominoes possible [8].

4. Extend the cube problem considered in §4-4 to a five-inch and a six-inch cube. Do you see a pattern emerging? Can you predict the outcomes for an n-inch cube?

5. Experiment with a paper-folding lesson with a class of slow learners and report upon your results.

6. Examine two general mathematics texts and compare their introductions to geometry. Report on any evidence you find in either book of the use of discovery techniques in introducing basic geometric concepts.

7. Read and report upon the unit on geometry prepared by the National Council of Teachers of Mathematics in their series *Experiences in Mathematical Discovery* [25].

8. Explore the experimental approaches used for developing geometric concepts by the School Mathematics Study Group in their text for average and below-average junior high school students [34].

chapter 5

Explorations with Computation and Mensuration

Slow learners are in desperate need of a review and relearning of the fundamental skills of arithmetic. This, however, needs to be done in disguised form if interest is to be maintained. The explorations suggested in this chapter provide a variety of opportunities for the development of arithmetic competence.

5-1 Finger Reckoning

Finger multiplication can be a fascinating topic taken just for fun. Here are two examples of a procedure for finding on one's fingers the product of any single-digit number and 9. Place both hands side by side, palms up.

To multiply 9 by 3, bend down the third finger from the left. Read the answer as 27, where the tens digit is found as the number of fingers to the

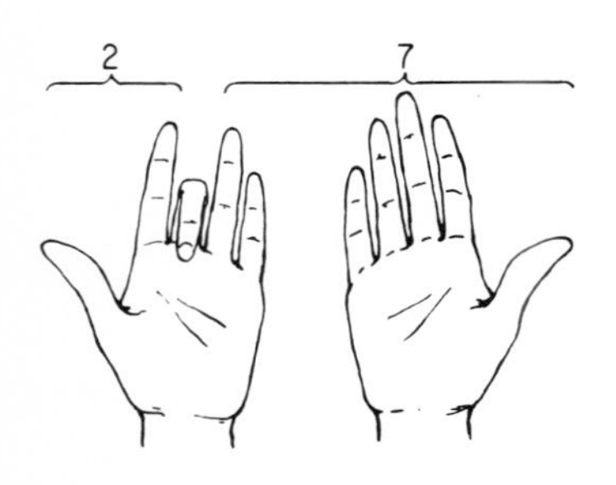

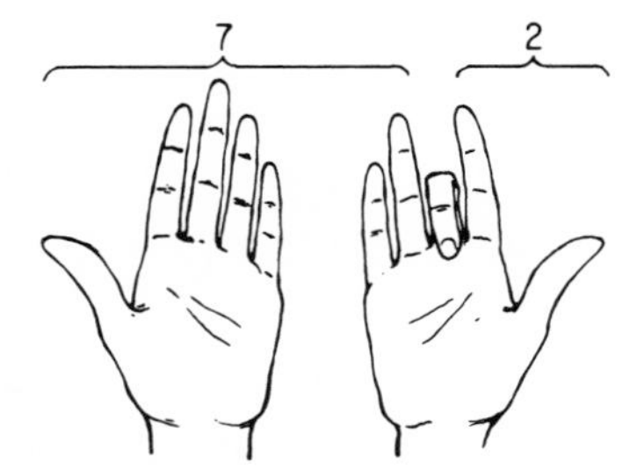

left of the bent finger, and the units digit is the number of fingers to the right of the bent finger.

To find the product 8×9, the eighth finger from the left is bent. Read the answer as 72.

This procedure can be extended to find the product of 9 and a two-digit number, provided that the tens digit is less than the ones digit. To find the product 9×38, put a space after the third finger from the left to represent the tens digit, 3. Represent the units digit, 8, by bending down the eighth finger from the left. Read the answer in groups of fingers, shown in the diagram, as 342.

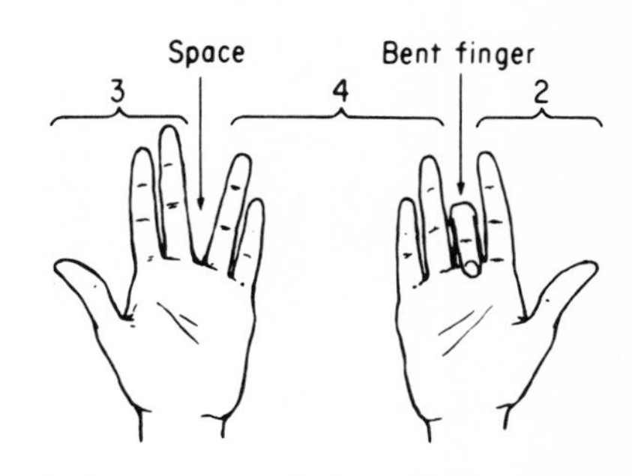

Another example of finger reckoning involves finding the product of any two numbers between 5 and 10 by a method that is claimed to be still in use by some European peasants. Begin with closed fists. Then on each hand raise a number of fingers corresponding to the difference between the given numbers and 5. For example, to multiply 6 by 8, raise one finger $(6 - 5)$ on one hand and three fingers $(8 - 5)$ on the other hand. The tens digit of the product is found as the sum of the raised fingers $(1 + 3)$, and the units digit is the product of the closed fingers (4×2).

5-2 Duplation and Mediation

The ancient Egyptians are said to have multiplied by a process of doubling. This process is based on the fact that any number may be represented as a sum of powers of 2. For example, $19 = 1 + 2 + 16$. Now to find the product 19×25 we proceed to double 25 as follows:

$$
\begin{aligned}
\textcircled{1} \times 25 &= \textcircled{25} \\
\textcircled{2} \times 25 &= \textcircled{50} \\
4 \times 25 &= 100 \\
8 \times 25 &= 200 \\
\textcircled{16} \times 25 &= \textcircled{400}
\end{aligned}
$$

To find the product 19×25 we add the multiples of 25 that correspond to 1, 2, and 16:

$$
\begin{aligned}
19 &= 1 + 2 + 16 \\
19 \times 25 &= (1 + 2 + 16) \times 25 \\
&= 25 + 50 + 400 = 475
\end{aligned}
$$

Here is another example. Consider the product 23×41.

(1) × 41 = (41)	23 = 1 + 2 + 4 + 16
(2) × 41 = (82)	23 × 41 = (1 + 2 + 4 + 16) × 41
(4) × 41 = (164)	= 41 + 82 + 164 + 656 = 943
8 × 41 = 328	
(16) × 41 = (656)	

A more refined and automatic procedure involves doubling one factor and halving the other. For example, to find the product 19×25 we may successively halve 19, discarding remainders at each step, and successively double 25 as follows:

19 ⟶ (25)	
9 ⟶ (50)	
4 100	
2 200	
1 ⟶ (400)	

Note: since all remainders are discarded, one-half of 19 is considered to be 9 and one-half of 9 is recorded as 4.

The process is complete when a 1 appears in the column of numbers which are being halved. Opposite each number in this column of halves there is a corresponding number in the column of numbers being doubled. The product 19×25 is found as the sum of the numbers that are opposite the odd numbers in the column of halves:

$$19 \times 25 = 25 + 50 + 400 = 475$$

Note that this process automatically selects the addends to be used in determining the product; one need not search for the appropriate powers of 2 to be used. When this process is used to find the product 23×41, we have:

23 ⟶ (41)	
11 ⟶ (82)	
5 ⟶ (164)	23 × 41 = 41 + 82 + 164 + 656 = 943
2 328	
1 ⟶ (656)	

5-3 Napier's Rods

The method for multiplication that appeared in one of the first published arithmetic texts in Italy in 1478 is an interesting one. It is referred to as

Gelosia multiplication. To multiply 837 by 492 using this method, first prepare an array as follows:

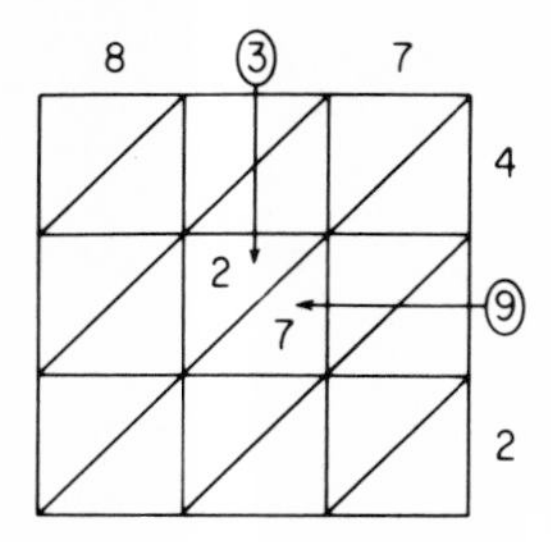

Then place the partial products involved in the multiplication in each individual cell. The placement for $9 \times 3 = 27$ is shown in the preceding figure; the completed entries are shown in the next figure. Note that the product 2×3 is recorded as 06 to show the absence of a tens digit. The slanting line in each cell separates the tens digit from the ones digit.

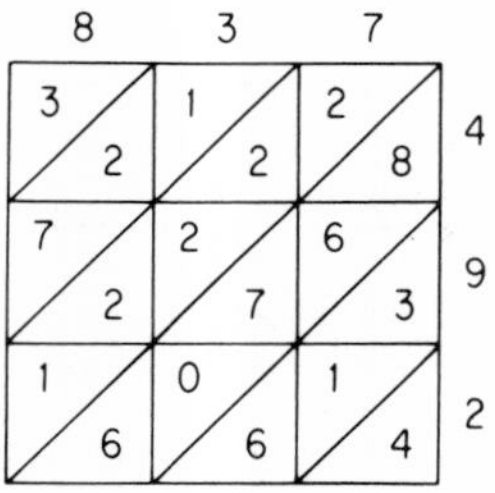

8	3	7	
3/2	1/2	2/8	4
7/2	2/7	6/3	9
1/6	0/6	1/4	2

To find the product, we now add along the diagonals, starting in the lower right-hand corner and carrying where necessary. We read the answer as indicated by the curved arrow.

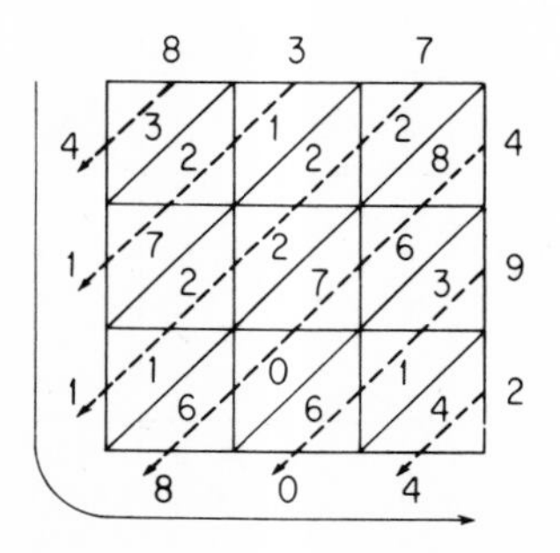

The procedure used in Gelosia multiplication may be justified in terms of our traditional algorithm. Note that the entries in each column correspond to the entries along the diagonals of the array that was used in the Gelosia method.

```
     837
    x492
      14 }
     06  }  2 x 837
    16   }
     63  }
    27   }  9 x 837
   72    }
    28   }
   12    }  4 x 837
  32     }
  411,804
```

The English mathematician, John Napier, extended this technique and developed a mechanical procedure for multiplication that is considered by some to be the forerunner of modern computing machines. First a set of strips are needed with the multiples of the digits 1 through 9, together with an Index, as in the next figure. These strips are often called **Napier's Rods** or **Napier's Bones.**

Index	1	2	3	4	5	6	7	8	9
1	0/1	0/2	0/3	0/4	0/5	0/6	0/7	0/8	0/9
2	0/2	0/4	0/6	0/8	1/0	1/2	1/4	1/6	1/8
3	0/3	0/6	0/9	1/2	1/5	1/8	2/1	2/4	2/7
4	0/4	0/8	1/2	1/6	2/0	2/4	2/8	3/2	3/6
5	0/5	1/0	1/5	2/0	2/5	3/0	3/5	4/0	4/5
6	0/6	1/2	1/8	2/4	3/0	3/6	4/2	4/8	5/4
7	0/7	1/4	2/1	2/8	3/5	4/2	4/9	5/6	6/3
8	0/8	1/6	2/4	3/2	4/0	4/8	5/6	6/4	7/2
9	0/9	1/8	2/7	3/6	4/5	5/4	6/3	7/2	8/1

To find the product 8×576, we place the rods headed by numerals 5, 7, and 6 alongside the Index as follows:

Index	5	7	6
1	0/5	0/7	0/6
2	1/0	1/4	1/2
3	1/5	2/1	1/8
4	2/0	2/8	2/4
5	2/5	3/5	3/0
6	3/0	4/2	3/6
7	3/5	4/9	4/2
→ 8	4/0	5/6	4/8
9	4/5	6/3	5/4

The product 8×576 may be read from the row beside 8 on the Index:

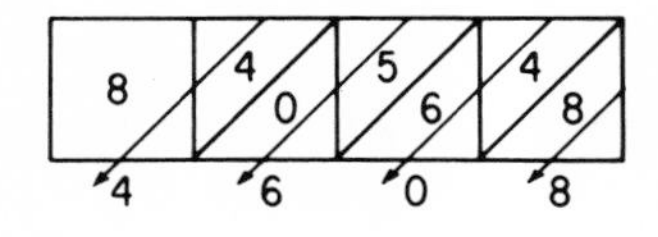

8 × 576 = 4608

Notice the similarity between this method and Gelosia multiplication. The product 4×576 may be read from the row beside 4 on the Index:

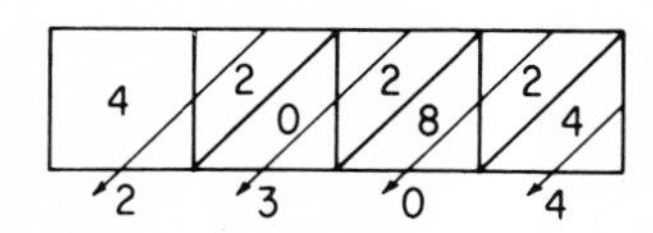

4 × 576 = 2304

With practice, youngsters can learn to compute rapidly with these strips, thereby enjoying mathematics while reviewing multiplication in a disguised form. It is this element of newness that is so important in stimulating and maintaining the interest of the slow learner. The teacher, however, has to build this up. Thus, for this unit, emphasis should be placed on the fact that the student is working with a forerunner of the modern giant computing machine!

5-4 Experiments with Measurement

The ability to use a ruler is one important skill that we wish to teach the low achiever. This seemingly simple skill is difficult for him to master because of the complex and large number of markings found on a typical ruler. A good way to present a unit in this area is to have the student first use a ruler calibrated only in inches, then one in half-inches, etc. These can be prepared on a ditto sheet, as follows, and then cut up and used one at a time.

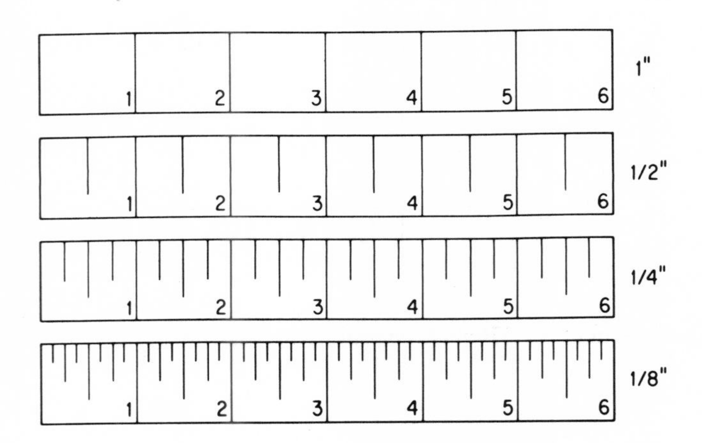

One cannot emphasize enough the importance of estimation of answers to problems, including those that involve measurement. A laboratory sheet as on page 43 serves as a good culmination of a unit on the use of a ruler. For better students, columns can be added to find the difference between their estimates and the actual measurements. Positive and negative signs can be used to indicate an overestimate or an underestimate.

The concept of measurement can be extended so as to develop many of the theorems of plane geometry through a laboratory experimental type of approach. The two classroom explorations on pages 45 and 46 illustrate the types of discoveries that one might reasonably expect slow learners to make on the basis of measurements taken for a specific set of figures.

Each of the following classroom explorations are designed for students to complete on their own in class.

Sample Classroom Exploration Involving Measurement of Line Segments

First estimate the length of each segment and record your estimate. Then measure each segment and record your measurement.

1. Estimate and measure to the nearest inch:

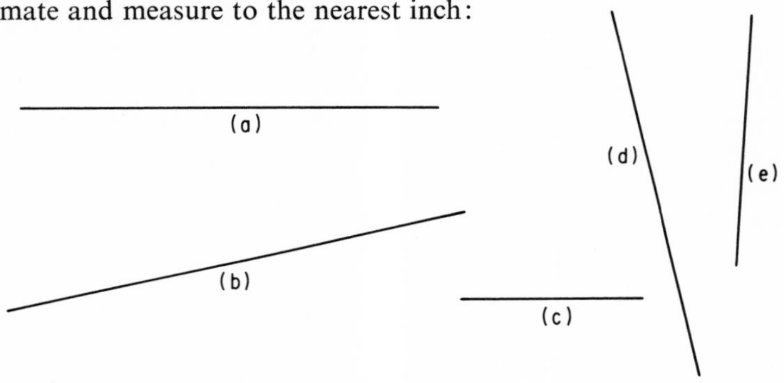

	Estimate	*Measurement*
(a)	_______	_______
(b)	_______	_______
(c)	_______	_______
(d)	_______	_______
(e)	_______	_______

2. Estimate and measure to the nearest half-inch:

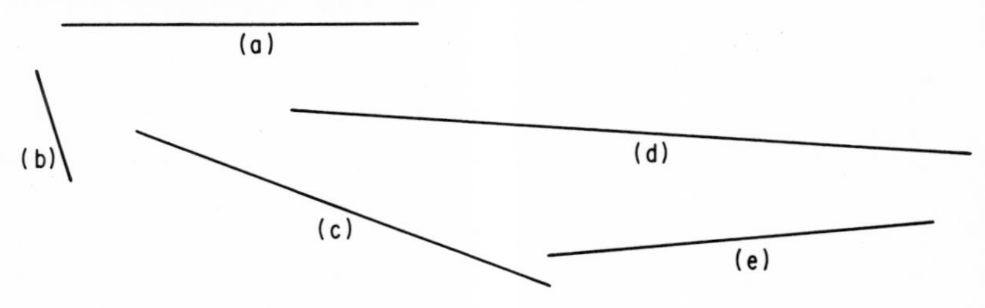

	Estimate	*Measurement*
(a)	_______	_______
(b)	_______	_______
(c)	_______	_______
(d)	_______	_______
(e)	_______	_______

3. Estimate and measure to the nearest quarter-inch:

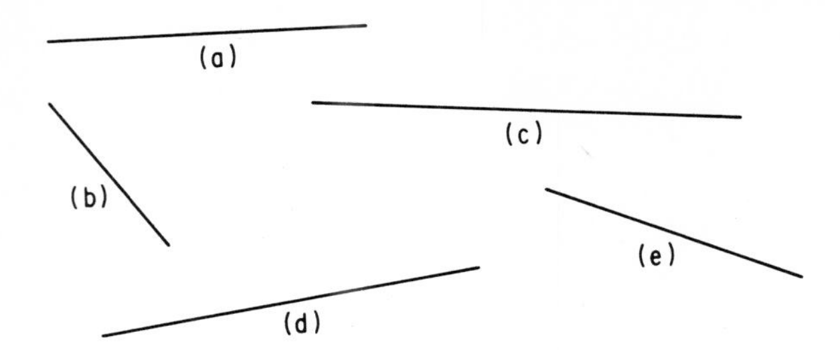

	Estimate	*Measurement*
(a)	______	______
(b)	______	______
(c)	______	______
(d)	______	______
(e)	______	______

4. Estimate and measure to the nearest eighth-inch:

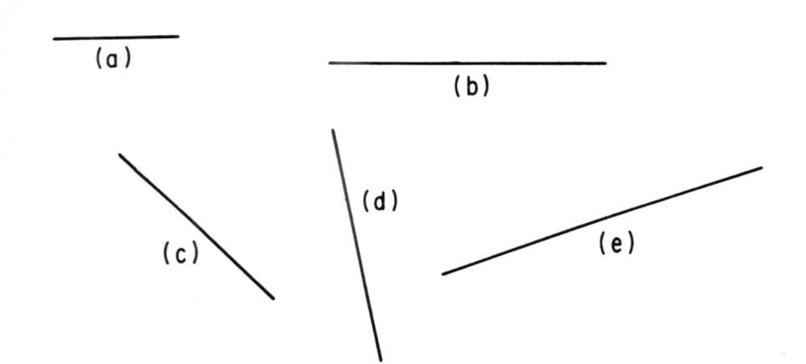

	Estimate	*Measurement*
(a)	______	______
(b)	______	______
(c)	______	______
(d)	______	______
(e)	______	______

Sample Classroom Exploration Involving Diagonals of Quadrilaterals

1. Each of the following figures is a quadrilateral. In each figure draw line segments AC and BD. These segments are the *diagonals* of the quadrilateral.

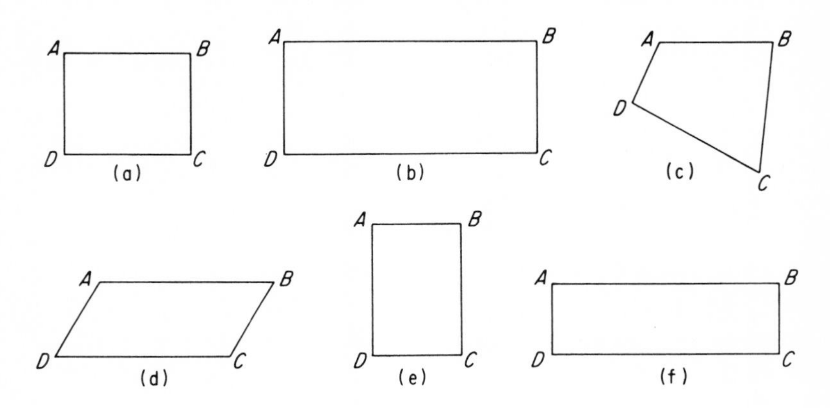

2. Measure, to the nearest eighth of an inch, the lengths of the two diagonals of each figure. Record your measurements in this table:

Figure	Length of $\overline{AC}$	Length of $\overline{BD}$
(a)		
(b)		
(c)		
(d)		
(e)		
(f)		

3. Compare the lengths of $\overline{AC}$ and $\overline{BD}$ in exercise 1. For which figures do the lengths appear to be equal?

4. Figures (a), (b), (e), and (f) are rectangles; Figs. (c) and (d) are not rectangles. Study the table of measurements obtained in exercise 2, and see if you can state a conclusion about the diagonals of a rectangle.

5. Draw two more rectangles and check the conclusion that you reached in exercise 4.

Sample Classroom Exploration Involving Right Triangles

1. Each of the following figures is a *right triangle* with a right angle indicated as ⊾. In a right triangle, the side opposite the right angle is the *hypotenuse.* In each triangle the hypotenuse is labeled as ______.

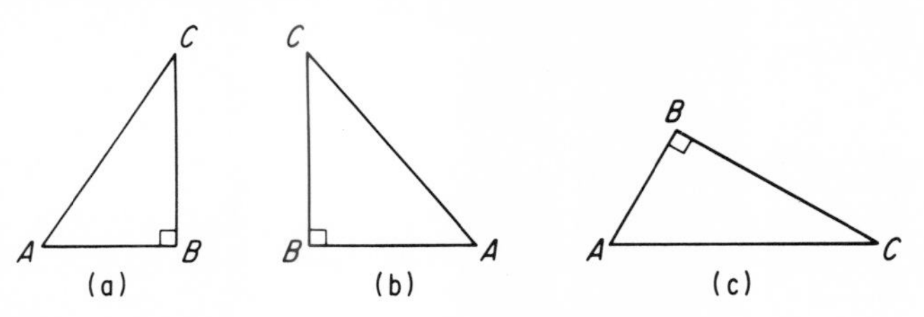

2. Bisect each hypotenuse and label the midpoint M.

3. Draw $\overline{BM}$ in each triangle. A line segment drawn from a vertex of a triangle to the midpoint of the opposite side is called a *median* of the triangle.

(a) How many vertices does a triangle have? ______

(b) How many medians does a triangle have? ______

4. Measure the length of the hypotenuse $\overline{AC}$ for each triangle; measure the length of the median to the hypotenuse $\overline{BM}$ for each triangle. Record your measurements in this table:

Triangle	Length of hypotenuse	Length of median
(a)		
(b)		
(c)		

5. Study the measurements you obtained in exercise 4, and try to draw some conclusion concerning the ratio of the length of the hypotenuse to the length of the median to the hypotenuse of a right triangle.

6. Construct a right triangle, bisect the hypotenuse, and draw the median from the vertex of the right angle. Take the necessary measurements and check the conclusion that you found in exercise 5.

Classroom exploration sheets similar to those just shown can be developed for many other facts from plane geometry. For example, the following facts are well suited to a discovery approach:

(1) The diagonals of a parallelogram bisect each other.

(2) The opposite sides of a parallelogram are equal in length.

(3) The line joining the midpoints of two sides of a triangle is equal in length to one-half of the third side.

Certainly it is easier to just tell these facts to your students. But learning is far more effective, exciting, and pleasurable if the student is able to make these discoveries on his own. Such techniques are highly recommended for slow learners, and, at appropriate grade levels, for all learners. This approach provides an excellent basis for a unit of study based upon individual explorations which the student can complete on his own and at his own rate of speed, thereby maintaining his interest.

5-5 Elementary Surveying

There is hardly anything more important in the teaching of mathematics to slow learners than building up their egos and giving the course an air of prestige and respectability. A unit on elementary surveying can serve this purpose very well. Of course it is not really "surveying" in the usual sense of the word, but this is the language to use to impress the youngsters!

Since this unit requires outdoor work, it is essential that careful planning be done to insure good class control. Furthermore, the unit needs to be preceded by one wherein scale drawings are studied and measurement is discussed. The student can be motivated to learn this material by the promise of its future application.

Assume that the necessary preparations have been made, that we now wish to find the height, x, of a flagpole, and that we are standing at a point, P, 50 feet from the base of the pole. Our distance from the base should be along level ground so that a right angle is formed with the flagpole and the distance can readily be measured by the students with a tape measure.

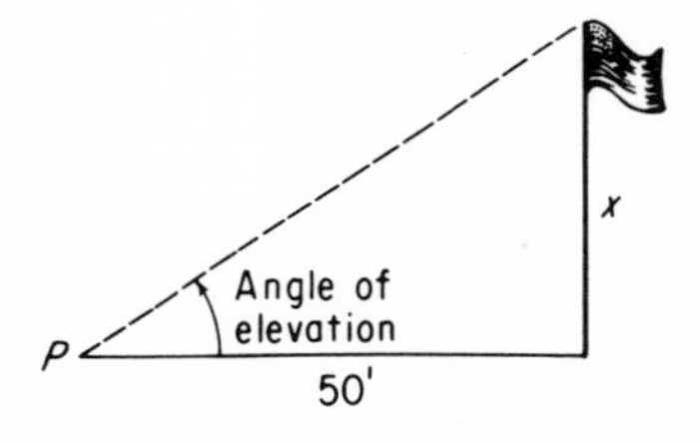

If, somehow, we can find the angle of elevation of the top of the pole from point P, then we can find x by making a simple scale drawing on graph paper. To find this angle of elevation we shall use an instrument called a **clinometer**, which each student should construct for himself. For very low ability groups the teacher may wish to use a commercial model or to have several home-made models prepared in advance. Here are the steps to follow in the construction of a clinometer.

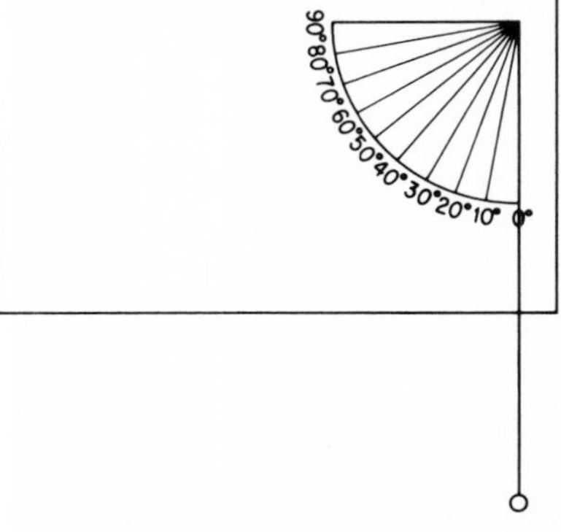

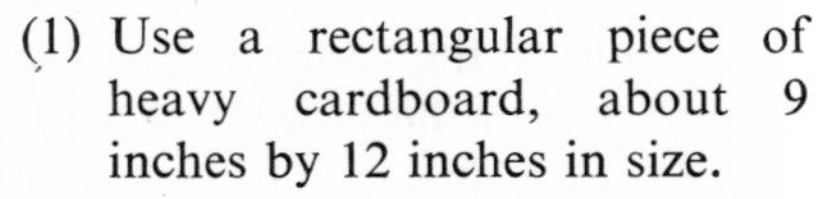

(1) Use a rectangular piece of heavy cardboard, about 9 inches by 12 inches in size.

(2) As in the figure, place a protractor close to the edge in the upper right-hand corner. Alternatively, draw a 90° arc and subdivide this into degrees as shown.
(3) At the vertex of the angle attach a string with a weight at the end.

To use the clinometer, the student stands at point P and sights along the edge of the instrument to the top of the flagpole. (Some ingenious youngsters will place a straw along the top to sight through. Others will place the instrument on a pivoted stand which can rest on the ground.)

The string will remain in a vertical position because of the weight attached, and it will cross the protractor at a point that represents the measure of the angle of elevation. The following figure shows the position of the clinometer for a reading of an angle of elevation of 40°.

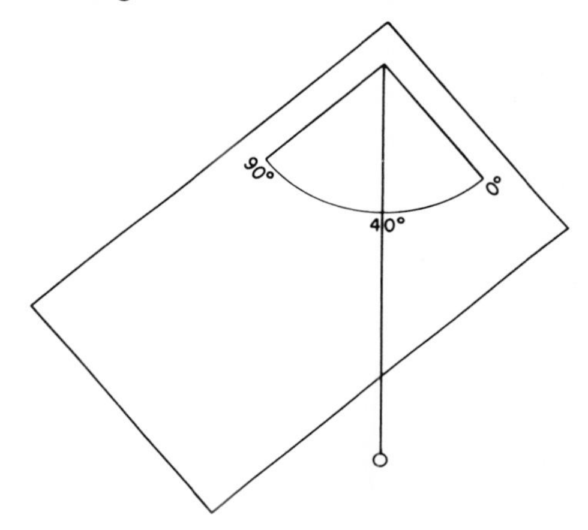

A sketch of a student 50 feet from a flagpole and making a sighting of the top of the pole is shown in the following figure.

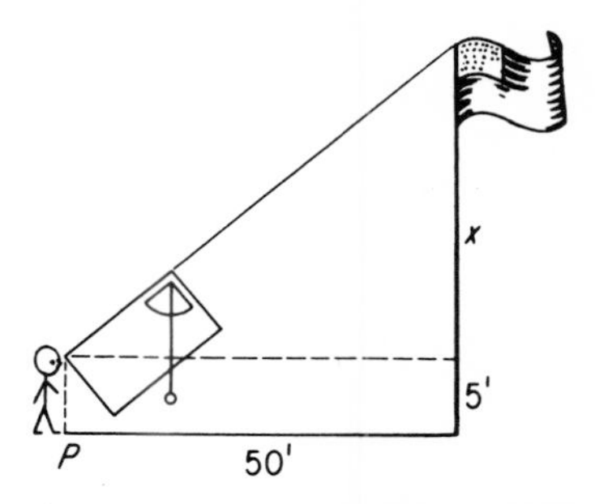

Note that construction of a scale drawing using 40° and 50 feet as two measurements will actually give the height of the flagpole above the student's horizontal line of sight. To find the actual height of the flagpole, it is necessary to know the distance from the student's eye to the ground. Assuming that this distance is 5 feet, we complete the scale drawing as in the next figure, using a convenient scale such as 10 feet per inch. The height of the flagpole is approximately 47 feet.

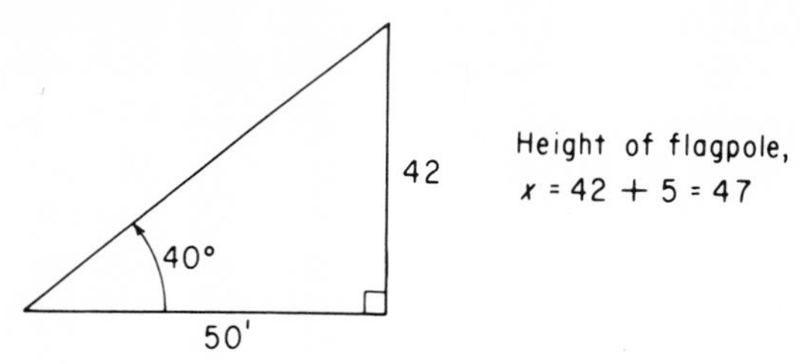

5-6 Nomographs

Nomographs are mechanical computational devices which slow learners will enjoy making and using. It is convenient to construct nomographs on graph paper. The scales in the following figure form a nomograph which may be used to find the sum of two positive integers less than or equal to ten.

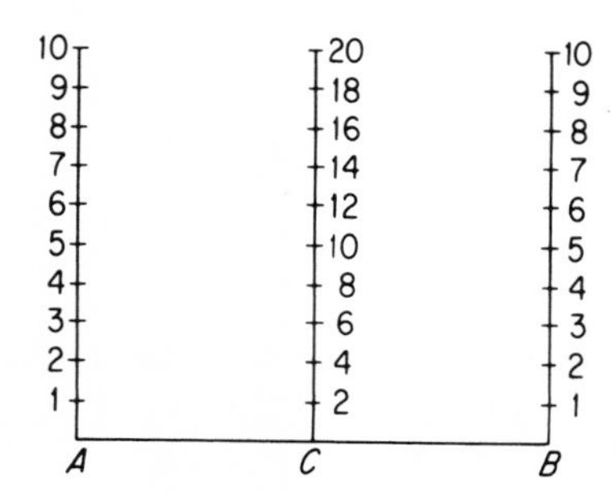

Notice in the figure that C is the midpoint of line segment AB. At points A, B, and C, scales are drawn perpendicular to $\overline{AB}$ and are identified as scale A, scale B, and scale C. Scales A and B are drawn using the same unit, and this unit is twice the one used on the C scale.

To find the sum $a + b$ of two numbers, we draw a line (or place a ruler) from a on the A scale to b on the B scale. The sum $a + b$ is read at the point where the line crosses the C scale. The sum $3 + 9$ is shown in the following figure:

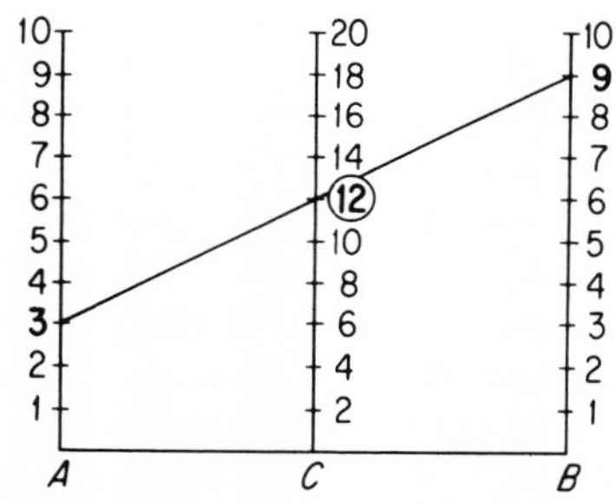

The scale of the nomograph shown may be extended for larger positive numbers and also to include negative numbers, thus providing an interesting introduction to this topic. The use of such a nomograph to find the sums $(-4) + 6$ and $(-8) + 2$ is shown in the next figure:

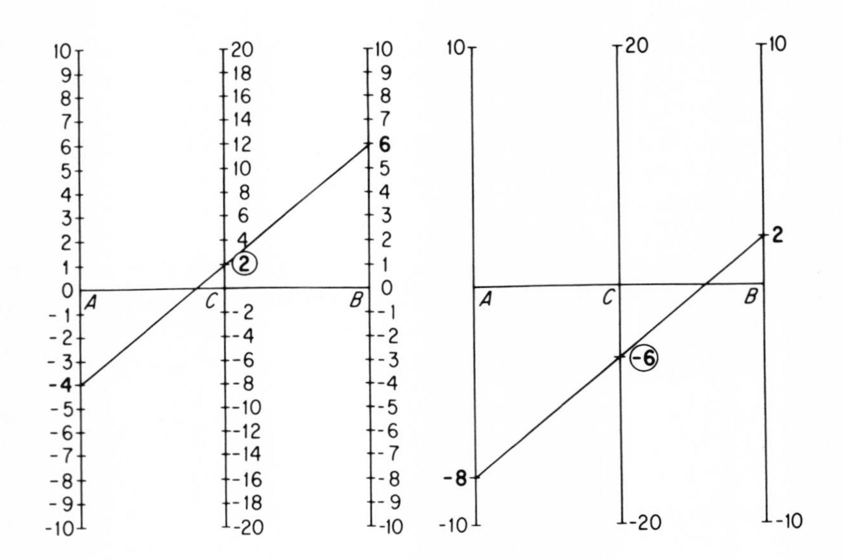

The nomographs shown in the preceding figure may be used for subtraction as well as for addition. Since $a + b = c$ if and only if $b = c - a$, we can locate c on the C scale, locate a on the A scale, and read the difference $c - a$ from the B scale. For example, to find the difference $12 - 3$, locate 12 on the C scale and 3 on the A scale. If a line is drawn through these two points, the line will cross the B scale at the difference, 9. Similarly, to find the difference $2 - (-4)$, locate 2 on the C scale, -4 on the A scale, and read the difference, 6, on the B scale.

5-7 Summary

The need for a concentrated review of the fundamentals of arithmetic for the slow learner cannot be overemphasized. On the other hand, the student who has failed to master these fundamentals for many years will become quite discouraged and subsequently disinterested in mathematics if he is asked to review these items in the traditional manner. Therefore the teacher must search for new ways and means of providing for this review "in disguise." Several suggestions along these lines have been set forth in this chapter.

Measurements and the use of a ruler are additional skills that the slow learner needs to master. Again, techniques have been suggested, with an emphasis upon the development and use of planned explorations, which the teacher may develop so as to teach geometric concepts through an active discovery-type approach to learning.

The reader may refer to the books by Meserve and Sobel, [22] and [23], for further reading on many of the items cited in this chapter. For additional references in the area of teaching geometry by means of classroom explorations, see the texts produced by the School Mathematics Study Group [34] and the unit on geometry by the National Council of Teachers of Mathematics in their series *Experiences in Mathematical Discovery* [25]. See [10] for a reference on nomographs.

Questions for Discussion

1. Find and report on at least one other finger-reckoning device.
2. Prepare a unit on ancient methods of computation for a slow junior high school class. If possible, teach this unit and report on your results.
3. Prepare a set of laboratory sheets similar to the ones of §5-4 and based on the facts listed on page 46. If possible, duplicate these and use them in a general mathematics class.
4. Prepare a bulletin-board display on measurement. (A good source of material is the set of charts on history of measurement distributed by the Ford Motor Co. of Dearborn, Michigan.)
5. Prepare a plan concerned with an out-of-doors lesson on surveying. If possible, teach the lesson and report on your results.
6. Find and describe methods of ancient computation other than the ones cited in this chapter or used in your answer for exercise 2.
7. Explain why the nomographs described in §5-6 work. Construct at least one other nomograph and explain its use.

chapter 6

Explorations in Probability

A unit on probability can do more to generate interest in mathematics with a group of slow learners than units on almost any other single topic. It can also help to develop a feeling of prestige for a course while at the same time serving as a vehicle for an otherwise dull review of some of the fundamentals of arithmetic. Furthermore, the entire area of probability and statistics can be justified as proper material for a general mathematics course from the point of view of its cultural and practical value for every citizen in our modern society.

6-1 Effective Procedures

To be effective and to stimulate interest, a unit on probability should be presented by means of an experimental, laboratory-type approach. That is, not only does the teacher talk about the probability of obtaining two heads in a single toss of two coins, but the students perform experiments to compare *expected* versus *actual* frequencies of such an event.

How does one start and develop a unit on probability? Here are several possible approaches, although one would not normally use all of these in any single presentation.

(1) Raise questions for class discussion and allow this discussion to be free and unstructured. For example:

> "I've just tossed this coin nine times and all of the tosses were heads. How would you bet on the tenth toss?"

Such a question can lead to discussion of the meaning of probability, what a probability of $\frac{1}{2}$ means, whether a coin has a "memory," the possibility of a biased coin, and the meaning of equally likely events.

(2) Present the class with one of the novel aspects of probability. For example, in a class of thirty the students would guess that there is little likelihood that two members would share the same birthday. Actually, for a group of thirty, the probability that this event will occur is 0.71; for forty the probability is 0.89. For the teacher, it is a relatively safe bet to make such a prediction. The odds are even more on your side if you predict that two members of the class have birthdays on the same or on adjacent dates.

(3) Provide a problem that creates interest, such as the following:

> There are three cards in a hat. The cards are identical except for color. One is red on both sides; one card is white on both sides; the third card is red on one side and white on the other side. One card is selected from the hat at random and placed on a table; the upper side of the card is red. What is the probability that the other side is also red?

Most youngsters (and teachers) will argue that the answer to this problem is $\frac{1}{2}$ since the other side must be either red or white. This can then lead to a discussion of **sample spaces** where all possible outcomes are listed. For the problem that has just been stated, we may use subscripts to identify the sides of the same color and obtain:

Card 1	*Card 2*	*Card 3*
R_1	W_1	R_3
R_2	W_2	W_3

If a red side is showing it must be R_1, R_2, or R_3. Here is a listing of the possibilities.

Side showing	*Opposite side*
R_1	R_2
R_2	R_1
R_3	W_3

There are three possible ways in which a card could be placed on the table with a red side up. In two of these cases the opposite side is also red; in the third case the opposite side is white. Therefore the answer to the original question is that the probability is $\frac{2}{3}$! This result does not fit the intuitive expectation of many students. There will be arguments and disagreements among the students—this is desirable. Capitalize on any such display of interest.

(4) Here is a final example of an approach to a unit on probability that usually generates interest. Consider a game that consists of selecting one winning slip of paper from a set of ten slips. You and one of your students will alternate in selecting one of the ten slips; the winner is the first one to pick the marked slip. The question for discussion is whether you should make the first selection, or whether the student should go first, or whether it matters at all who should go first.

After allowing time for a discussion of the pros and cons, suggest another game. Again, the object of the game is to pick the marked slip of paper. This time, however, slips will be selected alternately until all ten have been taken. At that time both contestants will examine their slips to see who has the winning paper. Again, raise the same question as to the advantages of going first.

Finally, propose the same game with a new rule. This time each contestant will select five pieces of paper, and then proceed to examine these to determine who has the winning slip. Does it matter who goes first?

Experience has shown that students will become involved in heated discussions of such games, thereby motivating a study of a unit on probability. For the game just described, all three versions are essentially equivalent, and it does not matter who makes the first selection. The probability of selecting the marked slip is the same whether you go first or second!

The reader will undoubtedly think of other ways to introduce a unit on probability. The important thing to remember is that the success or failure of such a unit can depend upon the manner in which the unit is initiated. Give the students an opportunity to discuss controversial problems, or allow them to engage in laboratory experiments such as those to be discussed in the following sections. The unit must not involve excessive computation or numerous rules of operation.

6-2 Explorations with Dice

A pair of dice on the teacher's desk will arouse interest, if not the concern of the administration! Multicolored blocks or hexagonal pencils serve the same purpose, but are not nearly as close to the youngsters' world of experience as a pair of dice. As illustrated in §6-1, specific questions can be raised for discussion, such as the probability of throwing a 7 in one toss of the dice. Let the students guess at the answer, and allow them to modify their guesses after several of them have each tossed the dice a number of times in class and the outcomes have been recorded on the board. (The occasional use of a pair of "loaded" dice by the teacher can lend even further interest to this approach!) Finally, determine the answer by means of a sample space.

One way to do this is through use of a **tree diagram.** As an aid to the explanation, consider one die to be red and the other die to be green. Note that there are 36 possible outcomes for a pair of dice, and that six of these produce 7's. Therefore the probability of throwing a 7 in one toss of the dice is $\frac{6}{36}$, or $\frac{1}{6}$.

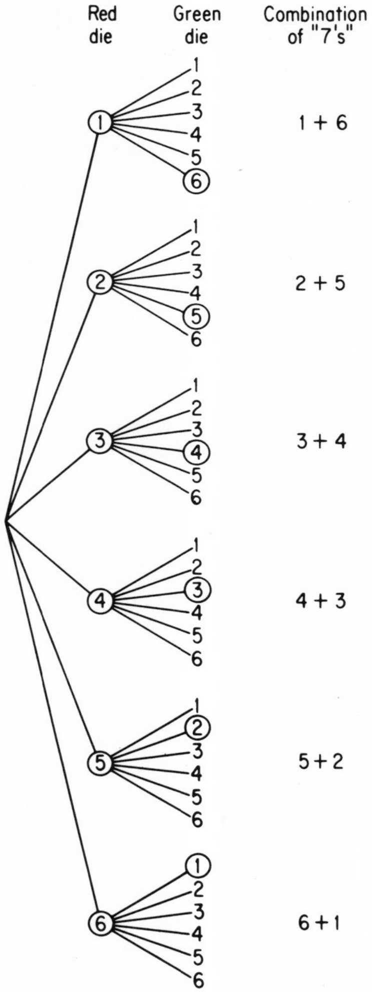

Red die	Green die	Combination of "7's"
1	1, 2, 3, 4, 5, (6)	1 + 6
2	1, 2, 3, 4, (5), 6	2 + 5
3	1, 2, 3, (4), 5, 6	3 + 4
4	1, 2, (3), 4, 5, 6	4 + 3
5	1, (2), 3, 4, 5, 6	5 + 2
6	(1), 2, 3, 4, 5, 6	6 + 1

An alternative representation of the sample space for the problem of tossing a 7 is shown in the following figure. Here the 36 possibilities are represented by the 6 × 6 array of dots, and the successful outcomes are represented by the solid dots.

This array leads to, or can follow from, a discussion of ordered pairs of numbers. The set of ordered pairs that give a sum of 7 is:

$$\{(1, 6), (2, 5), (3, 4), (4, 3), (5, 2), (6, 1)\}$$

That is, again, 6 of the 36 possible pairs of numbers have a sum of 7, and the probability of tossing a 7 is therefore $\frac{6}{36}$, or $\frac{1}{6}$.

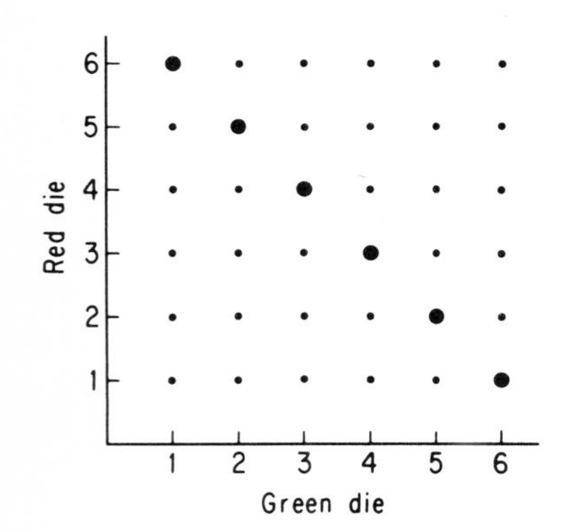

Several other probabilities can be found from the same array. For example, the probability of tossing a 9 is $\frac{4}{36}$ (that is, $\frac{1}{9}$) since the set of ordered pairs with 9 as their sum has four elements:

$$\{(3, 6), (4, 5), (5, 4), (6, 3)\}$$

The discussion of tosses of pairs of dice can be concluded with a class experiment in which students work in groups to toss dice and compare expected frequencies with observed frequencies. For example, in 36 tosses we might expect to obtain six 7's "on the average." It is important for youngsters to discover that fluctuation is normal, but within limits. Some groups may come up with six 7's, others with four or five 7's. But we should become suspicious if a group were to produce ten 7's or no 7's. Such outcomes are, of course, possible but highly improbable. Analogies to similar problems in everyday life can readily be made at this point.

6-3 Experimental Probability

There are many events for which the probability of success can only be determined experimentally. For example, for a given set of thumbtacks, one normally does not know the probability of obtaining a "head."

The only way to determine the probability of obtaining a head is to toss tacks until you see a trend. In a class you can allow groups of students to do this and combine all their results. Thus if 100 tosses were to produce 79 heads, we would say that the probability of heads is about $\frac{79}{100}$. Later and further experimentation may, of course, alter this estimate. With events of this type, however, we can find such answers only by an experimental approach.

Head: Tail:

Another interesting experiment is to determine the probability of obtaining a head on the spin of a coin on a smooth table. Of course one would normally predict the answer to be one-half, but not all coins are perfectly balanced. As a result, for certain coins the outcomes obtained experimentally will often differ significantly from one-half, a fact that will surprise and interest most people. For such experiments it is best to use newly minted coins which have not been worn smooth with use.

6-4 Explorations with Coins

Tossing coins is probably the most effective procedure that can be used to establish basic principles of probability. One possible approach would include the following activities.

First, establish a sample space for the tossing of two coins:

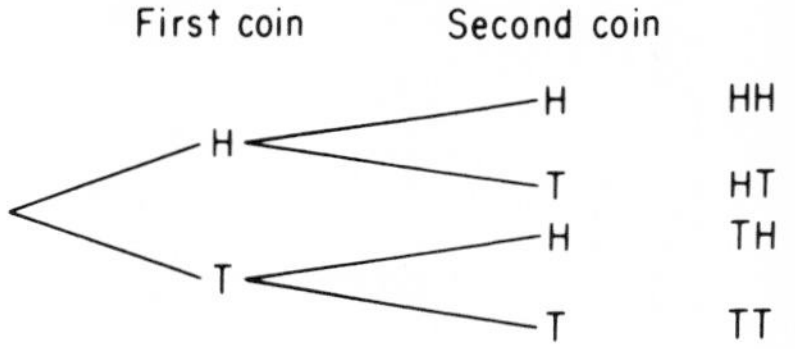

First coin	Second coin	
H	H	HH
H	T	HT
T	H	TH
T	T	TT

From this tree diagram the following **probability distribution** can be prepared:

Event	*Probability*
0 heads	$\frac{1}{4}$
1 head	$\frac{1}{2}$
2 heads	$\frac{1}{4}$

If we apply this distribution to a set of twenty tosses of two coins, we find that the *expected* distribution of heads is:

Event	*Frequency*
0 heads	5
1 head	10
2 heads	5

Next, allow groups of students to toss two coins twenty times and to keep a record of the results obtained. There will undoubtedly be some differences in the results. Minor fluctuations should normally be expected. If the results of all the groups are combined, the probabilities of 0, 1, and 2 heads should be approximately $\frac{1}{4}$, $\frac{1}{2}$, and $\frac{1}{4}$, respectively.

The same experiment can be repeated for three coins. The sample space would then be as follows:

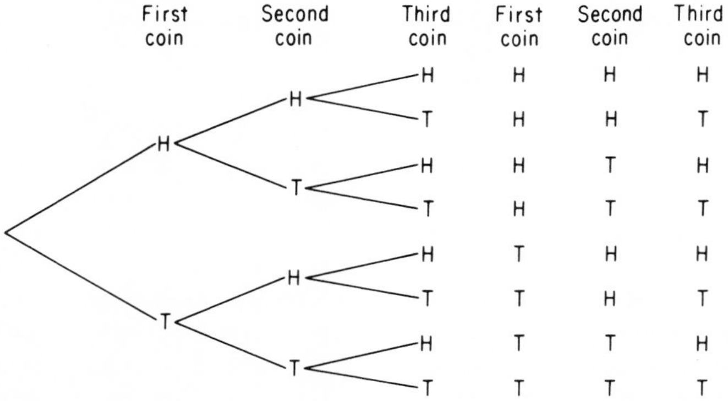

First coin	Second coin	Third coin	First coin	Second coin	Third coin
H	H	H	H	H	H
		T	H	H	T
	T	H	H	T	H
		T	H	T	T
T	H	H	T	H	H
		T	T	H	T
	T	H	T	T	H
		T	T	T	T

From this tree diagram we may obtain the following probability distribution:

Event	*Probability*
0 heads	$\frac{1}{8}$
1 head	$\frac{3}{8}$
2 heads	$\frac{3}{8}$
3 heads	$\frac{1}{8}$

If three coins are now tossed forty times, the expected distribution of heads would be as follows:

Event	*Frequency*
0 heads	5
1 head	15
2 heads	15
3 heads	5

Once again, to be effective, this theoretical discussion must be followed by actual experimentation in order to discover how close actual frequencies compare with expected ones.

In each case, both for two coins and for three coins, note that the sum of the probabilities is 1; that is, no other possibilities exist outside of the ones listed. Also note that for two coins there were four possible outcomes; for three coins there were eight possible outcomes. In general, for n coins there are 2^n possible outcomes.

6-5 Tables and Graphs

A very interesting experiment can be conducted involving tosses of a single coin. Results can be charted on a table such as the following, where the cumulative ratios of heads, tails, and percent of heads and tails are shown.

Number of throws	1	2	3	4	5	6	7	8	9	10
Head	×	×		×			×		×	×
Tail			×		×	×		×		
Ratio of heads	$\frac{1}{1}$	$\frac{2}{2}$	$\frac{2}{3}$	$\frac{3}{4}$	$\frac{3}{5}$	$\frac{3}{6}$	$\frac{4}{7}$	$\frac{4}{8}$	$\frac{5}{9}$	$\frac{6}{10}$
Ratio of tails	$\frac{0}{1}$	$\frac{0}{2}$	$\frac{1}{3}$	$\frac{1}{4}$	$\frac{2}{5}$	$\frac{3}{6}$	$\frac{3}{7}$	$\frac{4}{8}$	$\frac{4}{9}$	$\frac{4}{10}$
Percent of heads	100	100	67	75	60	50	57	50	56	60
Percent of tails	0	0	33	25	40	50	43	50	44	40

Note the excellent means this provides for a study of fractions, ratios, and percents.

The graphical presentation of the results obtained from these ten tosses gives a visual interpretation of the meaning of probability. In the long run, the graph of the percent of heads and the graph of the percent of tails will come closer and closer to the fifty-percent line, even though they continue to fluctuate. That is, in the long run we expect to come close to having one-half of our tosses produce heads and one-half produce tails, as in the following figure for the data in the table.

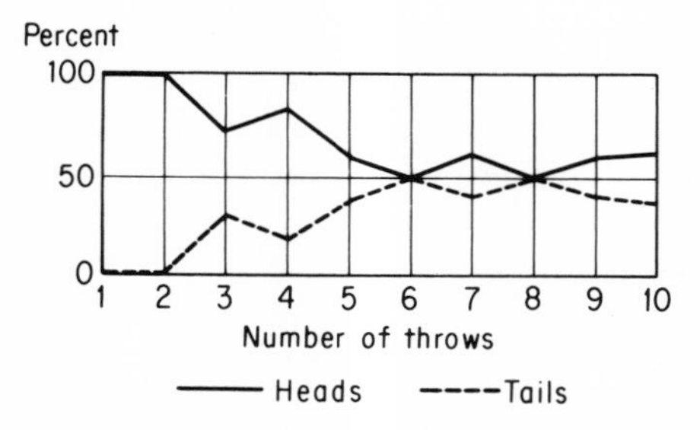

The student can now be asked to complete a chart of his own, or to extend this one for another ten tosses. This helps develop the concept of probability as meaning "probability in the long run." In other words, the fact that the probability of obtaining a head on one toss of a die is $\frac{1}{2}$ does not imply that one will obtain exactly five heads in ten tosses. Rather, it means that the longer one continues to toss a coin, the closer one can expect to come to having fifty percent of the tosses produce a head.

It can be established mathematically that if 100 coins are tossed, one can expect to obtain between 45 and 55 heads approximately $\frac{2}{3}$ of the time, between 40 and 60 heads approximately 95 percent of the time, and between 35 and 65 almost 100 percent of the time.

An interesting assignment is one that asks the students to toss 100 coins (or one coin for 100 tosses, ten coins for ten tosses, etc.) and count the number of heads. Before asking for the results, the teacher can predict the outcome by means of the mathematical expectation just described.

6-6 Sampling

Here is an example of an experiment that involves sampling and that may be conducted in a classroom.

First prepare an envelope with ten white and forty red chips. (Marbles, beads, colored slips of paper, and so forth may be used in place of chips.) Mix the chips thoroughly; then have a student remove a sample of five chips. Record the number of white chips obtained, return the chips to the box, mix, and draw again. Repeat for twenty drawings of samples. After twenty such samples, the percent of white chips in the box is to be estimated. (This information is not given to the student in advance.)

Now add to the original distribution a collection of fifty white chips without telling the class the nature of the contents of this addition. Have them draw another twenty samples of five each in the manner described before and form another estimate of the contents of the envelope.

This experiment should demonstrate that fluctuation is normal, but that this variation takes place about the average. For the initial distribution of ten white and forty red chips, we can expect, in the long run, that about one out of every five of the chips will be white; for the second distribution, that about three of every five of the chips will be white. Nevertheless, it is possible to draw a sample from the first distribution which contains three white chips; similarly, a sample from the second distribution may have only one white chip. It would be unusual, however, to draw a sample from the first distribution with four or five white; it would also be unusual to have a sample from the second distribution with zero white. There is a normal variation which emphasizes the meaning of probability as being the expected occurrence whenever there are many repeated trials.

The following is a set of instructions which might be given to a class if this specific experiment is to be conducted under a typical laboratory situation. Each student or group of students is to be supplied with a manila envelope containing ten white and forty red chips. In addition, each manila envelope is to contain a white enevelope in which there are fifty additional white chips.

Sample Classroom Instructions for a Laboratory Experiment

Read the following set of instructions carefully before you begin the experiment. As the class period progresses, refer to these notes whenever any question arises as to procedure.

Part I:

1. Open the manila envelope and withdraw the white envelope which is contained inside. Do not look inside at the contents of either of these two envelopes. (They contain chips that are either white or red.) Set the white envelope aside temporarily. Reach inside the manila envelope and mix the chips well.
2. Reach inside the manila envelope and take a sample of five chips. Count these before you look at them. Then look at the chips you have drawn, and record the number of white chips in this sample.
3. Return the chips which you have drawn, mix well, and then draw another sample of five. Record the number of white chips in this second sample.

4. Continue this process for a total of twenty samples. Each time a sample of five is drawn, the number of white chips is recorded and the chips are replaced in the envelope and mixed well.

Part II:

Method of recording data:

Have the data recorded on one sheet of graph paper for each student or group of students having a manila envelope. On the horizontal axis, number the drawings of samples from one to twenty. On the vertical axis, number from one to five to represent the number of white chips drawn in each sample. Then plot each sample by means of dots. A typical chart might appear as follows:

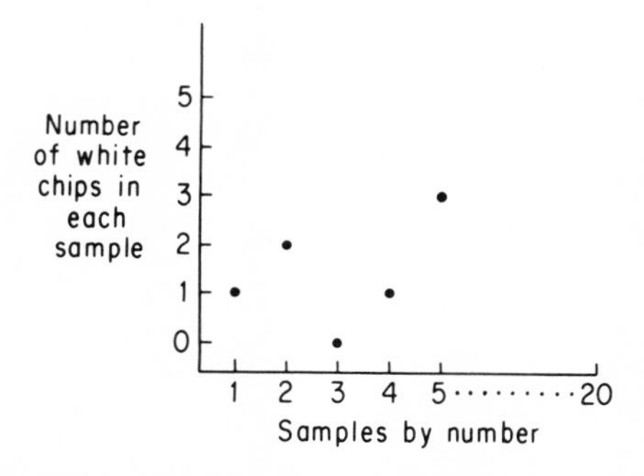

In the samples recorded on the chart, there was one white chip in the first sample, two in the second, none in the third, one in the fourth, and three in the fifth.

After you have completed the chart for your samples, stop and examine it carefully. On the basis of your twenty samples, make a prediction about the number of white chips in the manila envelope as compared to the total. That is, try to predict what percent of the chips in the envelope are white. Make this a group decision which is arrived at by means of discussion and by examination of your chart.

Part III:

1. Open the white envelope but do not look at its contents. Pour the chips from the white envelope into the manila envelope, and spend several moments mixing well.
2. Repeat the steps from the first part of the experiment; that is, take twenty samples of five chips each from the envelope, and record the results for this second distribution on a chart similar to that used for the first distribution.

After you have completed the second chart, make a prediction concerning:

(a) the percent of the chips in the second distribution which are white;
(b) your notion as to the contents of the white envelope.

Finally, examine the two charts you have drawn. In what ways are they alike? In what ways do they differ?

6-7 Summary

One of the most effective means of stimulating the interest of slow learners in mathematics is through the use of a unit on probability. Apparently there is something about the concept of "chance" that excites their imagination. As with other topics previously mentioned, such a unit must be developed by means of an experimental, laboratory point of view if it is to prove successful in motivation of learning.

Coins and dice are the two most readily available and commonly understood media for experimentation. However, if community or administrative pressure dictates that these not be used, other substitutes can be found such as thumb tacks, sugar cubes, and hexagonal-shaped pencils. A set of multicolored chips or slips of paper can also be used for sampling experiments.

The Institute of Life Insurance will supply teachers with classroom quantities of two booklets, [16] and [17], which introduce concepts of life insurance by means of a discussion of probability. Each booklet is a unit of study and includes both classroom exercises and activities that are appropriate for the slow learner. Background information for teachers can be found in the texts by Meserve and Sobel, [22] and [23]. A discussion of the birthday problem and other suggested experiments can be found in the text by Mosteller, Rourke, and Thomas [24]. The book by Gamow and Stern [7] is another excellent source of interesting problems and paradoxes in probability such as those presented here in §6-1. Still others can be found in the text by Northrop [29]. See the unit on arrangements and selections produced by the NCTM in *Exerpiences in Mathematical Discovery* [25].

Misuses of statistics and popular misconceptions concerning the laws of probability are interestingly presented in the two books by Huff, [14] and [15].

Questions for Discussion

1. Suggest ways of introducing a unit on probability other than those listed in §6-1.

2. Develop a laboratory sheet for a class experiment in probability that involves tossing of thumbtacks. Use the experiment in a general mathematics class and report on the results.

3. Toss a coin twenty times and summarize your results in a table and graph such as described in §6-5. Repeat this experiment by spinning a new penny twenty times. (Use pennies from different years, including one from 1964, if possible) Compare your results.

4. What would you guess is the probability of finding two license plates with the same last two digits in the next twenty cars observed? Test your hypothesis by repeating this experiment at least ten times. Have each student in your class conduct the experiment, and then comment upon the results found.

5. Prepare a two-week unit of study on probability for a group of slow learners at the junior high school level. If possible, teach this unit and report on your results.

6. Write a lesson plan that involves a class experiment in probability based upon the tossing of three coins. If possible, teach from this plan and report on your results.

chapter 7

Explorations with Mathematical Systems

The topics suggested in this chapter once again provide an indirect method of reviewing the fundamentals of arithmetic in a setting that usually generates interest. In addition, however, a unit on mathematical systems can do much to provide slow learners with a better understanding of the properties of our own decimal system.

7-1 Clock Arithmetic

A **mathematical system** involves a set of elements, and one or more operations that combine any two of the elements. An interesting and quite concrete system with which to begin a unit with slow learners involves **clock arithmetic.**

If it is now 10 A.M., then in five hours it will be 3 P.M. We may write:

$$10 + 5 = 3 \text{ (on a 12-hour clock)}$$

Students should then be given an opportunity to complete similar exercises on the 12-hour clock, using a visual approach such as the following:

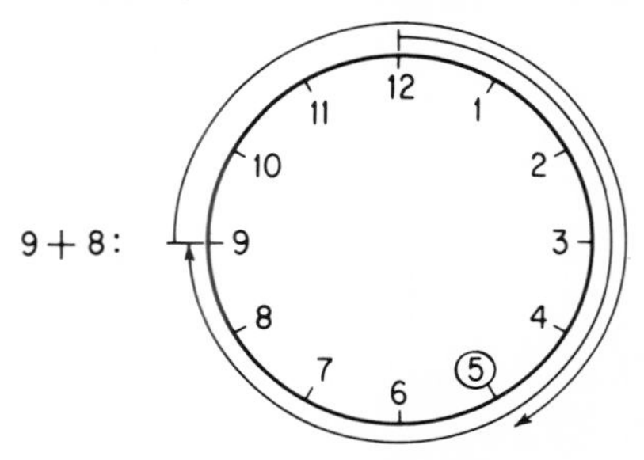

Note that addition is based upon counting in a clockwise direction, starting with 12 as the initial point. In the figure, we count 9 hours from 12, then continue for 8 more hours to complete the process at 5. Therefore $9 + 8 = 5$ (on a 12-hour clock).

After students have been given an opportunity to complete a number of such problems on a clock, they can be led to the development of a table of addition facts on a 12-hour clock such as the following:

+	1	2	3	4	5	6	7	8	9	10	11	12
1	2	3	4	5	6	7	8	9	10	11	12	1
2	3	4	5	6	7	8	9	10	11	12	1	2
3	4	5	6	7	8	9	10	11	12	1	2	3
4	5	6	7	8	9	10	11	12	1	2	3	4
5	6	7	8	9	10	11	12	1	2	3	4	5
6	7	8	9	10	11	12	1	2	3	4	5	6
7	8	9	10	11	12	1	2	3	4	5	6	7
8	9	10	11	12	1	2	3	4	5	6	7	8
9	10	11	12	1	2	3	4	5	6	7	8	9
10	11	12	1	2	3	4	5	6	7	8	9	10
11	12	1	2	3	4	5	6	7	8	9	10	11
12	1	2	3	4	5	6	7	8	9	10	11	12

Addition facts on a 12-hour clock

Multiplication on the 12-hour clock can be defined in terms of repeated addition. For example, 3×5 on the 12-hour clock is equivalent to $5 + 5 + 5$. Since $5 + 5 = 10$ and $10 + 5 = 3$, we know that $3 \times 5 = 3$ on the 12-hour clock. In a similar manner, $4 \times 7 = 4$ on the 12-hour clock. Allow the students to solve such problems directly by actually counting around a clock. Then, with teacher direction, attempt to have the students discover that clock arithmetic is really a system of remainders. That is, $4 \times 7 = 28$, and 28 represents two rotations around the clock with an excess of 4. It is this excess that gives the product, $4 \times 7 = 4$ (on the 12-hour clock).

As another example, consider the product 7×7:

$$7 \times 7 = 49 = 4 \times 12 + 1; \qquad 7 \times 7 = 1 \text{ (on the 12-hour clock)}$$

Some students will be able to complete a table of the multiplication facts on a 12-hour clock, and then explore the properties of such a table. For most classes, a discussion of addition and multiplication will suffice. Where feasible, one can introduce the concepts of subtraction and division as inverse operations performed by using the addition and multiplication tables. For example, on the 12-hour clock:

$$\text{since } 8 + 7 = 3, \text{ then } 3 - 7 = 8$$

$$\text{since } 4 \times 5 = 8, \text{ then } 8 \div 5 = 4$$

Subtraction lends itself very nicely to a visual approach as well, where we think of subtraction as motion in a counterclockwise direction. The problem, 3 — 7, is illustrated in the following figure:

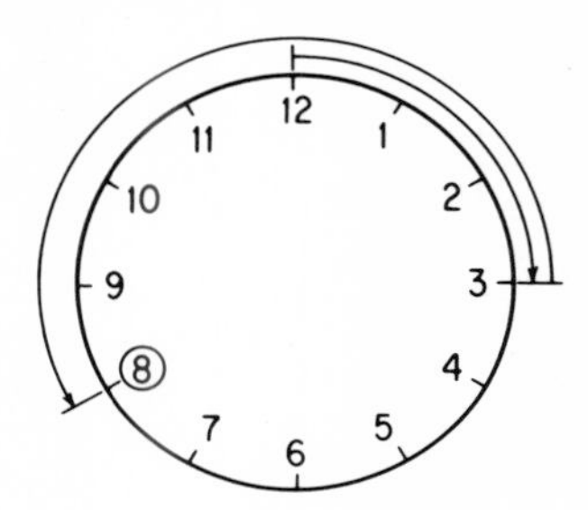

Count 3 units in a clockwise direction from 12 to 3. Then count 7 units in a counterclockwise direction. We complete the process at 8. Thus 3 — 7 = 8 (on the 12-hour clock).

It is important to note that a unit on clock arithmetic should not be taught for proficiency or memorization of facts on the 12-hour clock. Rather, the unit should serve as a means of review of some of the fundamental skills of arithmetic in a novel and interesting setting, with an emphasis on discovery of methods of operation and of basic properties of the system.

7-2 Modular Arithmetic

A somewhat more abstract mathematical system consists of a clock with positions numbered 0, 1, 2, 3, and 4 as in the figure. Addition on this clock may be performed as rotations in a clockwise direction. Thus 3 + 4 indicates

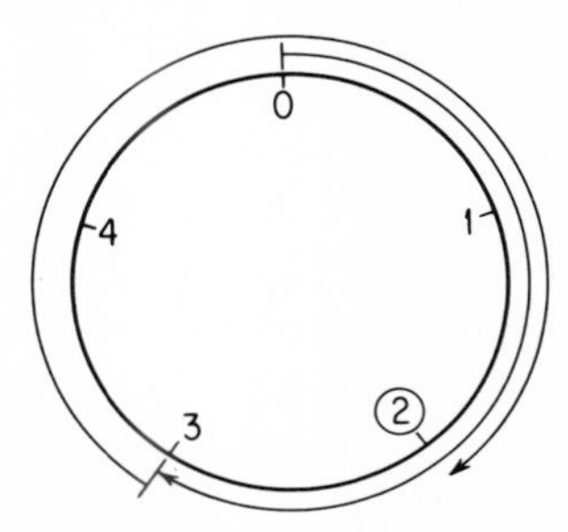

that one is to start at 0 and move 3 units, then 4 more units, to produce the result 2:

$$3 + 4 = 2 \text{ (on a 5-hour clock)}$$

The number 5 is often called the **modulus** of the system and is abbreviated as **mod 5.** Thus we may write the preceding fact as:

$3 + 4 = 2 \pmod 5$; read as "$3 + 4$ is equivalent to 2, mod 5"

Addition problems on a 5-hour clock can lead to the development of an addition table as follows:

+	0	1	2	3	4
0	0	1	2	3	4
1	1	2	3	4	0
2	2	3	4	0	1
3	3	4	0	1	2
4	4	0	1	2	3

Addition facts in mod 5 arithmetic

Multiplication is again defined as repeated addition. For example, 3×4 on the 5-hour clock is equivalent to $4 + 4 + 4$. Since $4 + 4 = 3$, and $3 + 4 = 2$, we see that $3 \times 4 = 2$ on the 5-hour clock. Students should be led to discover that this system, like the 12-hour clock, is based upon remainders. Thus $3 \times 4 = 12$, and 12 may be thought of as two rotations of 5 with a remainder of 2. As another example, consider the product 4×4:

$$4 \times 4 = 16 = 3 \times 5 + 1; \qquad 4 \times 4 = 1 \pmod 5$$

A table of multiplication facts for mod 5 arithmetic can readily be developed by the student and is given here for reference:

×	0	1	2	3	4
0	0	0	0	0	0
1	0	1	2	3	4
2	0	2	4	1	3
3	0	3	1	4	2
4	0	4	3	2	1

Multiplication facts in mod 5 arithmetic

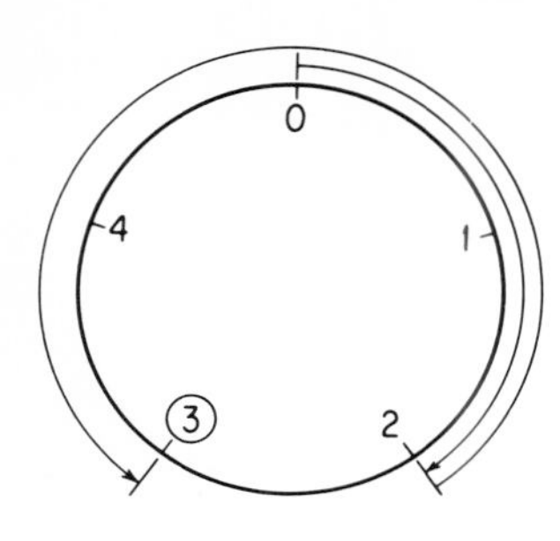

Subtraction and division can be performed as inverse operations of addition and multiplication by means of the given table of facts. For example, on the 5-hour clock:

$$\text{since } 3 + 4 = 2, \quad \text{then } 2 - 4 = 3$$

$$\text{since } 4 \times 4 = 1, \quad \text{then } 1 \div 4 = 4$$

Subtraction can be performed very easily directly on the clock. For example, to find the difference 2 − 4, first move 2 units in the clockwise direction. Then move 4 units in a counterclockwise direction. We complete the process at 3. Thus 2 − 4 = 3 (mod 5).

7-3 A System of Rotations

A mathematical system need not consist of numbers only. An interesting example of a nonnumerical system can be developed quite concretely in a classroom laboratory setting by having students note the various positions formed by the rotations of an index card. Begin by having each student label a card in each corner as in the first figure shown, and also write these same letters in the corresponding corners on the reverse side of the card for ease of reading when the card is turned over.

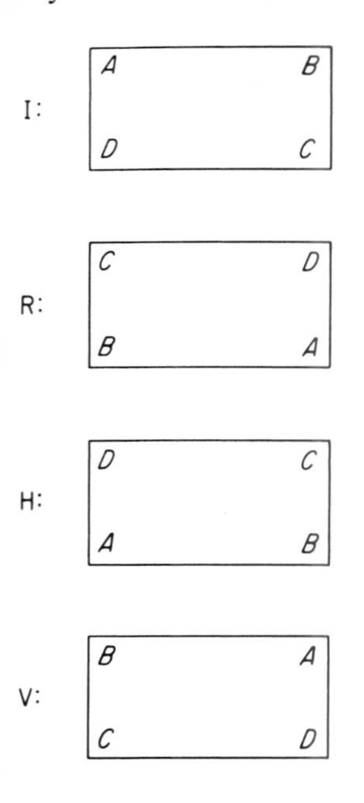

(1) The card is shown in its initial position. The movement *I* of a card leaves it in its initial position.

(2) The result of a rotation *R* of the card, from its initial position, 180° about its center is shown in this figure.

(3) The result of a rotation *H* of the card, from its initial position, 180° about its horizontal axis is shown in this figure.

(4) The result of a rotation *V* of the card, from its initial position, 180° about its vertical axis is shown in this figure.

Use the symbol $\sim$ to mean "followed by," and consider the possible ways in which the card can be rotated, as listed in the following table:

$\sim$	I	R	H	V
I				
R				
H				
V				

The direction $H \sim R$ means that the card is rotated about the horizontal axis, and this rotation is followed by a rotation of 180°. (Note that we always begin our sequence of rotations with the card in the initial position, I.) By actually performing the rotations with a card, the students will discover that $H \sim R = V$. That is, the two rotations, H and R, are equivalent to the single rotation, V. Similarly, they will find that $V \sim H = R$. Using a card, verify that each of the following entries is correct.

$\sim$	I	R	H	V
I	I	R	H	V
R	R	I	V	H
H	H	V	I	R
V	V	H	R	I

After completing the table, the student should be led by the teacher to discover as many properties as possible about this system. Here are several such properties that should become evident.

(1) Note the symmetry of the entries with respect to the diagonal of I's running from the upper left-hand corner to the lower right-hand corner. This is a clue that the set of rotations is **commutative** with respect to the given operation. Thus, for example, $H \sim R = R \sim H$.

(2) By testing several examples, we note that the system is also **associative.** That is, $H \sim (R \sim V) = (H \sim R) \sim V$.

(3) We also note: $I \sim I = I$; $R \sim I = I \sim R = R$; $H \sim I = I \sim H = H$; $V \sim I = I \sim V = V$. We call I the **identity element** for the system. It plays the same role that 0 plays for addition and 1 plays for multiplication in our decimal system of numeration.

(4) Every element has an **inverse**, or **opposite**, in this system. The opposite of I is I; the opposite of R is R since two rotations of 180° returns you to the initial position; the opposite of H is H since $H \sim H = I$; the opposite of V is V since $V \sim V = I$.

7-4 An Abstract Number System

As a final example of a mathematical system, appropriate after a unit on base five numeration, consider the following exploration which may be given to a class as a basis for discoveries of their own. This is a drastic extension of previous ideas, and the teacher will have to be ready to assist the very slow learner in making the appropriate discoveries.

SATURNIAN NUMBERS

On the planet Saturn, the inhabitants use a system of numeration that consists of the following set of symbols:

$$\{*, \triangle, \square, \#, Z\}$$

Here are some Saturnian addition facts:

$$\triangle + * = * + \triangle = \triangle$$
$$\square + * = * + \square = \square$$
$$\# + * = * + \# = \#$$
$$Z + * = * + Z = Z$$

What number does the numeral * represent? What can be said about the sum of any Saturnian number and * ?

Here are several other facts:

$$\triangle + \triangle = \square$$
$$\square + \triangle = \#$$
$$\# + \triangle = Z$$

What number does the numeral $\triangle$ represent? What numeral represents the sum $\triangle + \triangle + \triangle$? What is the sum $\triangle + \triangle + \triangle + \triangle$?

In Saturnian addition we also have:

$$Z + \triangle = \triangle *$$
$$Z + \square = \triangle\triangle$$

What are the sums $Z + \#$? $Z + Z$?

Copy and complete the following table of facts:

+	*	△	□	#	Z
*					
△					
□					
#					
Z					

How does this system compare with the base five system of numeration?

7-5 Summary

Although a unit on mathematical systems tends to be somewhat abstract, many teachers have found that the slow learner does enjoy working with abstractions as much as with concrete applications of mathematics. By using such techniques as clock arithmetic and rotations of a card, as described in this chapter, the unit can be made to have a concrete basis. As before, major emphasis should be given to actual classroom experimentation that leads to discovery of basic ideas.

Once the properties of a system have been discovered, they can be related to similar properties of the system of whole numbers, rational numbers, and real numbers, which are generally studied in many junior high school programs.

The teacher may find additional background in various mathematical systems in [22] and [23]. Also see the unit on properties of operations with numbers in the NCTM series *Experiences in Mathematical Discovery* [25].

Questions for Discussion

1. Prepare tables for addition and multiplication in mod 6 arithmetic.

2. Compare the properties of a mathematical system based on a 5-hour clock with one based on a 6-hour clock. How are they alike? How do they differ?

3. Prepare a classroom lesson on an original abstract number system similar to the one given in §7-4. Then teach the lesson and report on your results.

4. Here is a mathematical system consisting of movements of a soldier who begins in an initial position, E. R means right face, L means left face, and A means about face. The symbol "o" means "followed by." Thus $L \circ A$ means the soldier is to make a left face, followed by an about face. By actually performing these directions, verify that these two commands are equivalent to the single command, R, right face. What single command is equivalent to $L \circ L$? To $A \circ R$? To $R \circ R$?

5. Use the commands described in exercise 4 to complete the following table:

o	E	R	L	A
E				
R				
L				
A				

6. Present a one-day lesson to a class of slow learners on the mathematical system described in exercises 4 and 5 and report on your results.
7. Complete the table of Saturnian addition facts of §7-4.

chapter 8

Explorations with Mathematical Recreations

There is an almost inexhaustible supply of mathematical recreations that are suitable for use with slow learners. It is well for a teacher to have a collection of these ready for use in a wide variety of situations. They can be used on days preceding holidays, on days when shortened periods force the cancellation of other plans, and on regular days as well, as a change from daily routines. Some teachers use recreational material quite effectively as bulletin-board items and rotate this weekly. Others have been known to place these on index cards and then to give one to an individual student who may happen to finish an assignment or a test early. They also can serve occasionally as interesting homework assignments. Following is a sample of the variety of items possible.

8-1 Magic Squares and Arrays

Magic squares and arrays are of interest to most youngsters and provide a means of maintaining skills in arithmetic in a novel and disguised manner. Following are three examples that illustrate what can be done in this area.

(1) Place the numerals 1 though 9 in the adjoining cells so that the sum of the three numbers is 15 along each row, column, and diagonal.

(2) Place the numerals 1 through 6 in the circles so that the sum of three numbers along each side of the triangle is 12.

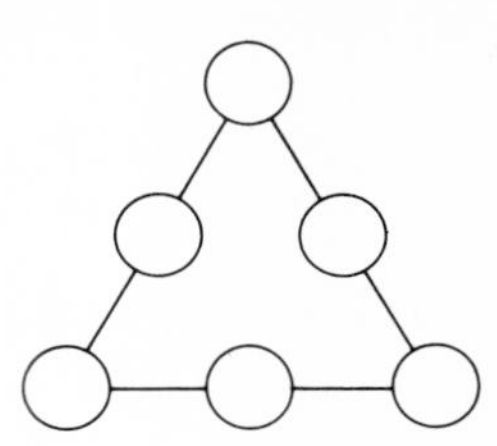

(3) Build a mathematical table wherein each entry is found, as in a regular addition table, by adding corresponding elements from each row and column. The original row and column numbers are chosen arbitrarily.

+	2	3	5	8
1	3	4	6	9
3	5	6	8	11
4	6	7	9	12
7	9	10	12	15

Now have someone circle any one of the numerals in the box and cross out all the others in that row and column. Below, the numeral 8 was selected.

+	2	3	5	8
1	3	4	6	9
3	5	6	8	11
4	6	7	9	12
7	9	10	12	15

Next repeat the process for a numeral that has not yet been crossed out until each numeral is circled or crossed out. In the figure that follows, the numerals 10, 12, and 3 were circled in that order. The sum of the circled numerals is 8 + 10 + 12 + 3 or 33. It is interesting to note here that the sum will always be 33, regardless of the selection one makes in circling and crossing out numbers. Furthermore, this sum is the same as the sum of the eight numerals outside of the square. It is not too difficult a task to show a group of slow learners why this will always work.

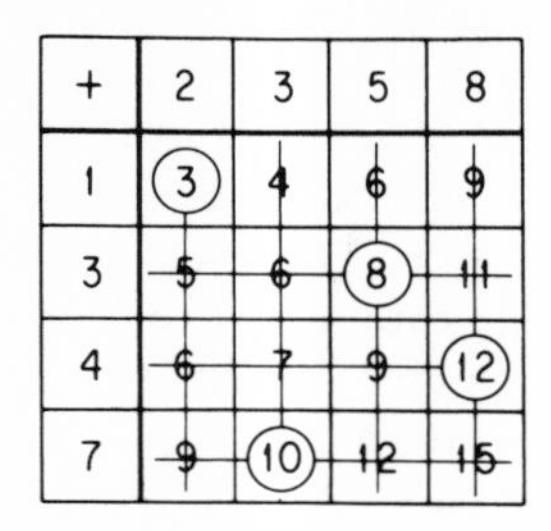

+	2	3	5	8
1	3	4	6	9
3	5	6	8	11
4	6	7	9	12
7	9	10	12	15

8-2 Mathematical Tricks

Mathematical tricks always serve to impress and to interest students of all levels of ability, especially the slow learner. Here are several examples:

(1) A popular trick is the "think of a number" type. For example, follow these instructions and your answer will always be 2, regardless of the number with which you start.

Think of a number.	x
Add 5 to this number.	$x + 5$
Multiply your answer by 2.	$2x + 10$
Subtract 6 from your answer.	$2x + 4$
Divide by 2.	$x + 2$
Subtract the number with which you started.	2

This can be explained to the slow learner by the use of algebraic symbols and by drawing pictures, as shown below. He can then attempt to compose similar tricks of his own.

Think of a number:	x	□	Number of marbles in a box.
Add 5:	$x + 5$	□ ○○○○○	Number of original marbles plus five.
Multiply by 2:	$2x + 10$	□ ○○○○○ □ ○○○○○	Two boxes of marbles plus ten.
Subtract 6:	$2x + 4$	□ ○○ □ ○○	Two boxes of marbles plus four.
Divide by 2:	$x + 2$	□ ○○	One box of marbles plus two.
Subtract the original number, x:	$(x + 2) - x = 2$	○○	Two marbles are left.

(2) Many tricks of magic have their basis in elementary mathematics. Here is a simple example of such a trick. Have someone place three dice on top of one another while you turn your back. Then instruct him to look at and find the sum of the values shown on the two faces that touch each other for the top and middle dice, the two faces that touch each other for the middle and bottom dice, and the value of the bottom face of the bottom die. You then turn around and at a glance tell him this sum. The trick is this: You merely subtract the value showing on the top face of the top die from 21. (Stack a set of three dice in the manner shown and try the trick; you will soon understand why it works.)

(3) Here is yet another trick. Ask someone to place a penny in one of his hands, and a dime in the other. Then tell him to multiply the value of the coin in the right hand by 6, multiply the value of the coin held in the left hand by 3, and add. Ask for the result. If the number given is even, you then announce that the penny is in the right hand; if the result is an odd number, then the penny is in the left hand and the dime is in the right hand.

8-3 Mathematical Games

Mathematical games can be fun. Here are three samples.

(1) Place a half-dollar, a quarter, and a nickel in a pile, with the largest coin at the bottom as in the figure. Try to move these coins, one at a time, to position C. (Coins may also be placed in position B.) At no time may a larger coin be placed on a smaller coin, and the task is to be completed in seven moves. Now place a penny on top of the pile and attempt to perform the same task in fifteen moves.

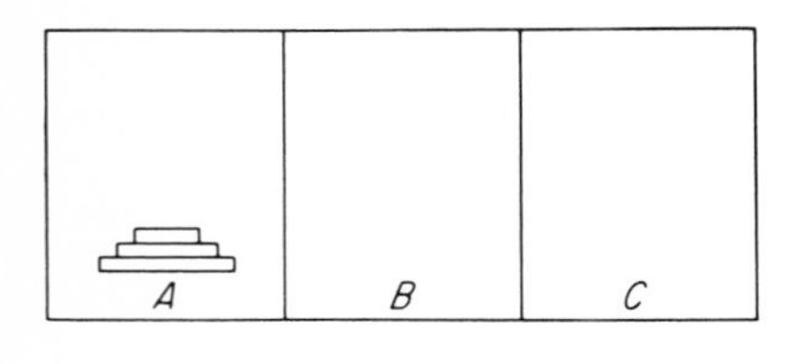

This is an example of a famous problem called the **Tower of Hanoi** problem. The ancient Brahman priests, it is said, were to move a pile of 64 discs of decreasing size in the manner indicated, after which the world would end. This task would require $2^{64} - 1$ moves. It is fun to estimate how long this would take at the rate of one move per second.

(2) Here is a game that two can play. The players alternate in selecting one of the numbers 1, 2, 3, 4, 5, or 6. After each number is selected, it is added to the sum of those previously selected. Thus, if player A selects 3 and player B selects 5, then the total is 8. If A selects 3, again the total is 11, and B goes. The object of the game is to reach 50.

There is a way to always win if you are permitted to go first. Select 1 and then be sure to select numbers to total 8, 15, 22, 29, 36, and 43. (Merely add the difference between 7 and your opponent's number. If he selects 2, you select 5; if he selects 3, you select 4; etc.) Once you arrive at 43, he cannot win. Whatever number he selects, you can always choose a number to total 50. Allow your students to discover your secret way of winning!

(3) Another interesting game that can be played in class and that has numerous possibilities is called "Guess My Rule." Ask one of the students to name two numbers; you respond with one number. Continue in this manner until some student thinks that he has discovered your rule for naming your number. Then test his discovery by asking him to respond to two numbers that you give.

There are many possible rules that the teacher can use, ranging from the very simple to ones that may prove to be too complex for the slow learner. It is well to start with a simple one, such as the sum of the two given numbers. For example, if the student gives 3 and 4, you respond with 7. From this lead into more complex ones such as the following:

(a) The sum of the given numbers increased by 1. For example, if 3 and 4 are the given numbers, the response is 8.
(b) One less than the sum of the given numbers. For example, for 3 and 4, the response is 6.
(c) One more than the product of the given numbers. For example, 3 and 4 gives 13.
(d) Two less than the product of the given numbers. For example, 3 and 4 gives 10.
(e) The larger of the given numbers. Thus 3 and 4 gives 4.
(f) The average of the given numbers. Thus 3 and 4 gives $3\frac{1}{2}$.
(g) The sum of the first number and twice the second number. Thus 3 and 4 produces $3 + 2(4)$, that is, 11. (This will prove to be very difficult for most slow learners.)

8-4 Mathematical Puzzles

Most students, slow as well as bright, are intrigued by mathematical puzzles. Fortunately, these are numerous and available from many sources. Here are a few classic examples:

(1) A farmer has to get a fox, a goose, and a bag of corn across a river in a boat which is only large enough for him and one of these three items. Now if he leaves the fox alone with the goose, the fox will eat the goose. If he leaves the goose alone with the corn, the goose will eat the corn. How does he get all the items across the river?

(2) Three Indians and three missionaries need to cross a river in a boat big enough only for two. The Indians are fine if they are left alone, or if they are with the same number or with a larger number of missionaries. They are dangerous if they are left alone in a situation where they outnumber the missionaries. How do they all get across the river without harm?

(3) A man goes to a well with three cans whose capacities are three gallons, five gallons, and eight gallons. Explain how he can obtain exactly four gallons of water from the well.

(4) Three men enter a hotel and rent a suite of rooms for $30. After they are taken to their rooms, the manager discovers he overcharged them; the suite only rents for $25. He thereupon sends a bellhop upstairs with the $5 change. The dishonest bellhop decides to keep $2 and only returns $3 to the men. Now the rooms originally cost $30, but the men had $3 returned to them. This means that they only paid $27 for the room. The bellhop kept $2. $27 + $2 = $29. What happened to the extra dollar?

(5) A man went into a shoestore and bought a $5 pair of shoes, paying for them with a $20 bill. The shoestore owner went next door to the grocer to get change for the bill and then gave the customer his $15 change. Later the grocer discovered that the $20 bill was counterfeit and the shoestore had to replace it with a good bill. How much did the shoestore lose in terms of money and merchandise in this whole transaction?

8-5 Summary

Mathematical recreations provide an excellent means of stimulating the interest of slow learners. These may be in the form of tricks, games, or puzzles. Indeed, some teachers make profitable use of a technique of having a "puzzle of the week" placed on the bulletin board to capture the attention and interest of the student. The reader would do well to begin collecting such recreations in order to accumulate a file for future use.

There are numerous texts available, many in paperback form, that deal with mathematical recreations. Several good sources of such items may be found in [3] and [11]. Also see Chapter 1 of [22].

Questions for Discussion

1. Give a solution for each of the first two examples of §8-1.

2. Complete a magic square using sixteen cells and the numerals 1 through 16.

3. Attempt to complete the Tower of Hanoi problem (§8-3) using a half-dollar, a quarter, a nickel, a penny, and a dime, in that order. You should be able to perform the task in $2^5 - 1$, that is 31, moves.
4. Provide solutions to each of the five puzzles of §8-4.
5. Prepare a set of five puzzles similar to those of §8-4.
6. Prepare a lesson plan for a full-period lesson based on the game "Guess My Rule" (§8-3). If possible, teach the lesson to a group of slow learners and report on your results.

Epilogue

The material presented in the preceding pages does not represent or even approach a textbook for the slow learner. This is an important project that still remains for the future. Rather, the material is intended as a series of ideas that teachers can use in preparing materials for classes of low achievers. Each suggested classroom procedure was selected because experience has proved it to be highly successful in motivating this group for learning mathematics. Furthermore, this material is by no means exhaustive. Until such time as published material is abundantly available, the individual teacher will do well to prepare his own units of study for at least part of each course. This source book of ideas, hopefully, should provide some clues as to possible areas of study for the low achiever.

Many significant questions are still hotly debated and argued. Despite the reports of many groups, and the opinions of educators interested in this area, the available experimental data and research have not yet provided completely acceptable answers to such questions as the following:

(1) Is one year of senior high school general mathematics enough for the nonacademic student?

(2) What should be the content of the general mathematics class in the ninth grade?

(3) If a four-year sequence is to be made available to the nonacademic student, what should be its content? Is the checklist of the Post-War Commission an adequate guide for the organization of the content for these youths?

(4) For the lower-ability groups, how much of algebra and geometry should be introduced? Can these pupils go beyond applied arithmetic, and should they?
(5) How much repetition of basic arithmetic should there be during the high school years?
(6) What constitutes an adequate program of remedial arithmetic in the secondary school? How shall such a program be organized?
(7) Is homogeneous grouping desirable?
(8) Should the mathematics for the slow or average pupil differ from that given for others in kind and/or amount?
(9) If more than one year of general mathematics is made available, what shall be the requirements to take courses beyond the ninth grade?
(10) Who should take general mathematics? Should pupils who are capable of taking the college preparatory sequence be permitted to enroll in such courses?
(11) What should a school do with pupils who wish to enroll in college preparatory courses but whose aptitude and/or achievement clearly indicate that success in such courses is improbable?
(12) What is the place, if any, of such courses as business arithmetic, vocational mathematics, and consumer mathematics?
(13) How can unfavorable attitudes towards mathematics be prevented and removed?
(14) What is the minimum mathematical competence for a high school graduate? Should all graduates be required to pass some minimum test in mathematics?
(15) What procedures are available to properly motivate and develop favorable attitudes among the slow learners?
(16) What teaching methods have proved to be most successful with the nonacademic student?
(17) What is the role of evaluation and marking practices for this group?
(18) What relative emphasis should be given to the practical applications of mathematics as opposed to pure subject-matter study?
(19) What procedures are available to lend prestige to "second track" courses?
(20) How may an adequate program of guidance be organized so that students are properly placed in the program, taking due account of both their ability and probable future needs?

The National Council of Teachers of Mathematics, through their Committee on Mathematics for the Non-College-Bound, is making an attempt to suggest and carry out activities and projects designed to learn the answer to these and other questions as well. In particular, they wish to test the hypothesis that experiences in the discovery of mathematical ideas will not only promote enthusiasm for the study of mathematics, but will also provide for greater retention of learning. Indeed, much of this book has been based on the assumption of this hypothesis, verified by the experience of many teachers working with slow learners.

There is room for much research and thought on the problems of teaching mathematics to our long forgotten friend, the slow learner. The rewards for one who engages in such research are unlimited in terms of the thanks that he will receive from the entire mathematical community!

Bibliography

1. Abbott, Edwin A., *Flatland.* New York: Dover, 1952.
2. Abraham, Willard, "The Slow Learner—Surrounded and Alone," *Today's Health*, Vol. XLIII (September, 1965), p. 59.
3. Adler, Irving, *Magic House of Numbers.* New York: Day, 1957.
4. Commission on Post War Plans, Guidance Report, *The Mathematics Teacher*, Vol. XL (1947), pp. 318–319.
5. Eves, Howard, *An Introduction to the History of Mathematics.* New York: Holt, Rinehart & Winston, 1953.
6. Featherstone, W. B., *Teaching the Slow Learner.* New York: Bureau of Publication, T. C., Columbia University, 1951.
7. Gamow, George and M. Stern, *Puzzle-Math.* New York: Viking, 1958.
8. Gardner, Martin, *The Scientific American Book of Mathematical Puzzles and Diversions.* New York: Simon and Schuster, 1959.
9. ______, *The Second Scientific American Book of Mathematical Puzzles and Diversions.* New York: Simon and Schuster, 1961.
10. Glenn, William H. and D. A. Johnson, *Computing Devices.* St. Louis: Webster, 1961.
11. ______, *Fun with Mathematics.* St. Louis: Webster, 1961.
12. ______, *Number Patterns.* St. Louis: Webster, 1961.
13. Greenholz, Sarah, "What's New in Teaching Slow Learners in Junior High School," *The Mathematics Teacher*, Vol. LVII, No. 8 (December, 1964), pp. 522–528.

14. Huff, Darrell, *How to Lie with Statistics*. New York: W. W. Norton and Co., Inc., 1954.

15. _____, *How to Take a Chance*. New York: W. W. Norton and Co., Inc., 1959.

16. Institute of Life Insurance, *Mathematics in Action*. New York: 1963.

17. _____, *Sets, Probability and Statistics*. New York: 1964.

18. Johnson, Donovan A., *Paper Folding in the Mathematics Class*. Pamphlet, National Council of Teachers of Mathematics, 1957.

19. Johnson, G. Orville, *Education for the Slow Learners*. Englewood Cliffs, N.J.: Prentice-Hall, 1963.

20. Jones, Burton W., *Elementary Concepts of Mathematics*. New York: Macmillan, 1963.

21. Kraitchik, M., *Mathematical Recreations*. New York: Dover Publications, 1953.

22. Meserve, Bruce E. and M. A. Sobel, *Introduction to Mathematics*. Englewood Cliffs, N.J.: Prentice-Hall, 1964.

23. _____, *Mathematics for Secondary School Teachers*. Englewood Cliffs, N.J.: Prentice-Hall, 1962.

24. Mosteller, F., R. E. Rourke, and G. B. Thomas, Jr., *Probability and Statistics*. Cambridge, Massachusetts: Addison-Wesley, 1961.

25. National Council of Teachers of Mathematics, *Experiences in Mathematical Discovery*. Washington, D.C.: 1966.

26. _____, *Preliminary Report of the Conference on the Low Achiever in Mathematics*. Washington, D.C.: 1964.

27. _____, "The Secondary Mathematics Curriculum," Report of the Secondary School Curriculum Committee, *The Mathematics Teacher*, Vol. LII, No. 5 (May, 1959) pp. 389–417.

28. New Jersey Secondary School Teachers Association, *The Slow Learner in Secondary Schools*, Yearbook, 1961.

29. Northrop, Eugene P., *Riddles in Mathematics*. Princeton, N.J.: Van Nostrand, 1944.

30. Potter, Mary and V. Mallory, *Education in Mathematics for the Slow Learner*. National Council of Teachers of Mathematics, 1958.

31. Schaaf, Oscar F., "Preparing the MNCB Text 'Experiences in Mathematics Discovery,'" *The Low Achiever in Mathematics*. Washington D. C.: U. S. Department of Health, Education and Welfare, 1965.

32. School Mathematics Study Group, "Conference on Mathematics Education for Below Average Achievers," April, 1964.

33. _____, *Introduction to Algebra*. Yale, 1962.

34. _____, *Introduction to Secondary School Mathematics*. Yale, 1962.

35. Sobel, Max A., "Getting Started in a Ninth Grade Non-Academic Class," *The Mathematics Teacher*, Vol. LII, No. 2 (February, 1959), pp. 143–146.

36. ______, "Providing for the Slow Learner in the Junior High School," *The Mathematics Teacher*, Vol. LII, No. 5 (May, 1959), pp. 347–353.

37. ______, "The 'M' Materials of SMSG," *The Low Achiever in Mathematics*. Washington D. C.: U.S. Department of Health, Education, and Welfare, 1965.

38. U. S. Department of Health, Education, and Welfare, Office of Education, *The Low Achiever in Mathematics*. Washington, D.C.: 1965.

Answers to Selected Questions for Discussion

Chapter 3—Explorations with Numbers and Numerals

1. **(1)** Approximately $11\frac{1}{2}$ days; **(2)** approximately 5000 feet, that is, about 1 mile; **(3)** approximately 6800 pounds; **(4)** approximately 100 miles; **(5)** approximately 91; **(8)** approximately 287,000,000.

3. $\frac{1}{1\cdot 2} + \frac{1}{2\cdot 3} + \cdots + \frac{1}{9\cdot 10} = (\frac{1}{1} - \frac{1}{2}) + (\frac{1}{2} - \frac{1}{3}) + \cdots + (\frac{1}{9} - \frac{1}{10}) =$
$\frac{1}{1} - \frac{1}{2} + \frac{1}{2} - \frac{1}{3} + \frac{1}{3} - \cdots - \frac{1}{9} + \frac{1}{9} - \frac{1}{10} = \frac{1}{1} - \frac{1}{10} = \frac{9}{10}$

4.

A	B	C	D	E
1	2	4	8	16
3	3	5	9	17
5	6	6	10	18
7	7	7	11	19
9	10	12	12	20
11	11	13	13	21
13	14	14	14	22
15	15	15	15	23
17	18	20	24	24
19	19	21	25	25
21	22	22	26	26
23	23	23	27	27
25	26	28	28	28
27	27	29	29	29
29	30	30	30	30
31	31	31	31	31

5. Several representative cards are as follows:

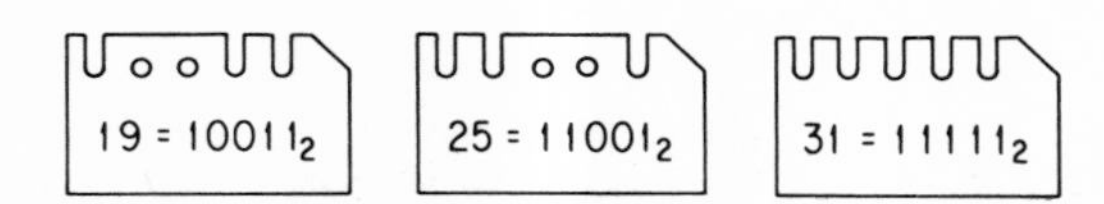

Chapter 4—Explorations with Geometric Figures

3.

4. The following table gives the data for a 3-, 4-, 5-, and 6-inch cube, as well as for an n-inch cube:

Size of cube	*Number of cubes with red paint on:*			
in inches	*0 faces*	*1 face*	*2 faces*	*3 faces*
3	1	6	12	8
4	8	24	24	8
5	27	54	36	8
6	64	96	48	8
⋮				
n	$(n-2)^3$	$6(n-2)^2$	$12(n-2)$	8

Chapter 5—Explorations with Computation and Mensuration

1. See [5].

2. See [5].

3. The nomograph is based on a property of trapezoids. In the figure, the length of the median, c, is equal to one-half the sum of the bases, a and b. Thus $2c = a + b$. By doubling the scale on C, we read the sum $a + b$ directly. See [10] for another example of a nomograph.

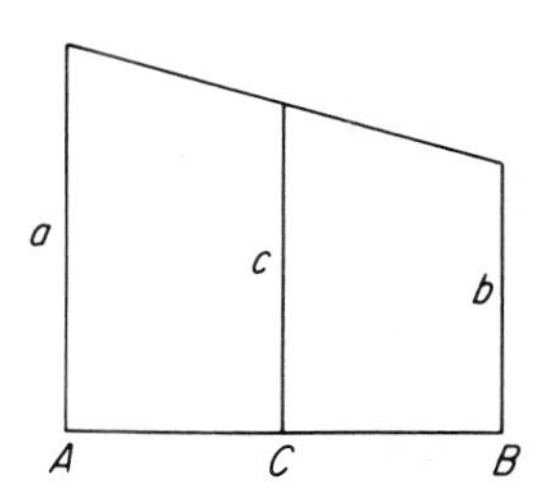

Chapter 6—Explorations in Probability

1. For suggested ideas, see the approaches developed in [16] and [17]. Also refer to [7] for interesting and novel problems in probability.

4. The probability is approximately 0.87.

Chapter 7—Explorations with Mathematical Systems

1.

+	0	1	2	3	4	5
0	0	1	2	3	4	5
1	1	2	3	4	5	0
2	2	3	4	5	0	1
3	3	4	5	0	1	2
4	4	5	0	1	2	3
5	5	0	1	2	3	0

Mod 6 addition

×	0	1	2	3	4	5
0	0	0	0	0	0	0
1	0	1	2	3	4	5
2	0	2	4	0	2	4
3	0	3	0	3	0	3
4	0	4	2	0	4	2
5	0	5	4	3	2	1

Mod 6 multiplication

2. The properties are the same except that not every element has an inverse with respect to multiplication on the 6-hour clock. Thus both are commutative and associative for addition and multiplication, and both contain identity elements (0 and 1) for both operations.

4. See array for exercise 5.

5.

o	*E*	*R*	*L*	*A*
E	*E*	*R*	*L*	*A*
R	*R*	*A*	*E*	*L*
L	*L*	*E*	*A*	*R*
A	*A*	*L*	*R*	*A*

7.

+	*	△	□	#	Z
*	*	△	□	#	Z
△	△	□	#	Z	△*
□	□	#	Z	△*	△△
#	#	Z	△*	△△	△□
Z	Z	△*	△△	△□	△#

This system is equivalent to a base five system of numeration where * = 0, △ = 1, □ = 2, # = 3, and Z = 4.

CHAPTER 8—EXPLORATIONS WITH MATHEMATICAL RECREATIONS

1. (1)

4	9	2
3	5	7
8	1	6

(2)

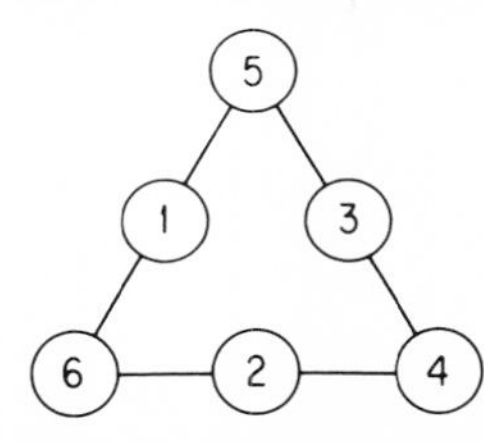

2.

1	12	7	14
8	13	2	11
10	3	16	5
15	6	9	4

The sum of the numerals in each row, column, and diagonal is 34. Other solutions are possible.

4. (1) The farmer crosses the river with the goose and returns. He then crosses with the fox and returns with the goose. He then crosses with the corn and returns. Finally, he crosses with the goose.

(2) Eleven trips are needed. First, one Indian and one missionary go over; the missionary returns. Then, two Indians go over and one returns. Next, two missionaries go over; one missionary and one Indian return. Two missionaries go over next, and one Indian returns. Then, two Indians go over and one of them returns. Finally, the last two Indians go over.

(3) Fill up the five-gallon can and use this to fill the three-gallon can. This leaves two gallons which you pour into the eight-gallon can. Repeat this procedure again and you will have four gallons in the eight-gallon can. (There are other ways as well.)

(4) There really is no missing dollar. The computation may be done in one of two ways: $(30 - 3) - 2 = 25$, or $25 + 2 + 3 = 30$. In the problem the arithmetic was done in a manner that is not legitimate, that is, $(30 - 3) + 2$.

(5) \$15 and a pair of shoes.

Index